THE
CARUS MATHEMATICAL MONOGRAPHS

Published by

THE MATHEMATICAL ASSOCIATION OF AMERICA

———

ANALYTIC FUNCTIONS
of a
COMPLEX VARIABLE

By

DAVID RAYMOND CURTISS

Professor of Mathematics, Northwestern University

Published for
THE MATHEMATICAL ASSOCIATION OF AMERICA
by
THE OPEN COURT PUBLISHING COMPANY
CHICAGO · ILLINOIS

Composed and Printed By
The University of Chicago Press
Chicago, Illinois, U.S.A.

PREFACE

The first of the Carus Monographs, Professor Bliss's *Calculus of Variations*, has for its successor the present volume on *Analytic Functions of a Complex Variable*. The reader is assumed to have the same preparation as for the preceding monograph, that is to say, an acquaintance with elementary differential and integral calculus. Without such knowledge one may, however, obtain some idea of the scope and purposes of the theory of functions from the following pages. Those should profit most who are familiar with more than the elements of the calculus.

The theory of functions of a complex variable has been developed by the efforts of thousands of workers through the last hundred years. To give even the briefest account of the present state of that theory in all its branches would be impossible within the limits of this book. What is attempted here is a presentation of fundamental principles with sufficient details of proof and discussion to avoid the style of a mere summary or synopsis. In various places there are indications of directions in which special portions of the subject branch off from the main stem. For almost every topic the reader is given several references; and, be it for better or worse, there are no footnotes.

The system of references perhaps needs some defense, certainly it requires explanation. Numerous citations of authorities are favorite means for an author to show his erudition—or someone's else. Perhaps this book goes to the opposite extreme and might well give a more complete statement of sources. However, the plan used in the following pages has been adopted because the writer believes that the greatest service he can do those for whom the book was intended is to induce them to supplement the reading of the present monograph by a study of accessible standard treatises on the subject. It is hoped thus to assist those who are not specialists in this field, but who are reading this book for a presentation of its general outlines, to study more fully certain details in which they may be interested, without the necessity of consulting memoirs difficult to obtain or difficult to read. Such hardships at least are avoided when references are confined to six volumes published in this country with one exception, and in the main understandable by those competent to read the present monograph.

Since the period of the development of the theory of functions has been coincident with the age of criticism in mathematics and the spirit of that age has been notably exemplified in this field, it may seem to those who have some acquaintance with this subject little less than sacrilege to start, as we do here, without precise definitions of fundamental notions such as curve or region. However, we have chosen to leave some of these ideas undefined, or but partially defined, in order not to repel the reader at the start by too great an appearance of formalism. Such omissions may be supplied by a reading of the books quoted as references.

D. R. Curtiss

Northwestern University
November, 1925

TABLE OF CONTENTS

CHAPTER I

ORIGIN AND APPLICATIONS OF THE THEORY

1. The development of the idea of analytic functions.
The first step toward a theory of functions of a complex variable was the introduction of the complex number in the solution of algebraic equations with real coefficients. The equation $x^2 - 2x + 5 = 0$, for example, has no real roots, but is formally satisfied by the expressions $1 \pm \sqrt{-4}$, or $1 \pm 2i$, where i stands for $\sqrt{-1}$, if the fundamental operations are suitably defined for these complex numbers. Soon it was perceived, and finally proved in a satisfactory way by Gauss shortly before the year 1800, that every algebraic equation with real coefficients has complex roots, real numbers being a special kind of complex numbers for which the coefficient of i is zero.

Progress was next made by associating complex numbers with plane geometry through Argand's scheme whereby a complex number $z = x + iy$ is represented by the point (x, y) in a system of plane Cartesian coordinates.

Geneva
1768-1825

A further step was at once suggested; z was made an independent variable by allowing x and y to vary freely, and functions $w = f(z)$ were studied. A very general interpretation of the term "function" would make any expression $w = u(x, y) + iv(x, y)$ a function of $z = x + iy$, provided the functions u and v have values that are defined for each pair of values x, y. The theory of such complex functions of the complex variable z would be identical with the study of real function pairs (u, v). Without further limitations we could have no such abundance of specific results as has distinguished what is generally styled the *theory of functions of a complex variable*.

The restriction which has been found so fruitful focuses consideration upon what are called *analytic functions*. With a natural definition of the derivative dw/dz, which will be explained later, we style a function *analytic* throughout a region in the (x, y) plane if its derivative exists at every point of the region. At once we obtain a class of functions with many remarkable properties not shared by complex functions in general. For example, if only the existence of the first derivative is postulated, it can be shown that all the successive derivatives exist; that there can be but one function analytic throughout a region including its boundary, which is equal to a given continuous function along the boundary; and that the values of an analytic function are determined at every point of its region of definition if the values of the function and of all its successive derivatives are given at one point. These theorems will serve to illustrate the highly restricted character of analytic functions.

But has the restriction been carried too far? Such a question is best answered by considering applications of the theory of analytic functions.

2. The usefulness of the theory. First let us note the answers given by this theory to questions arising as problems for functions of a real variable—not merely such comparatively formal ones as concern an extended definition of the function $\log x$ so that x may have negative real values, or of $\sin^{-1} x$ so that x may be greater than unity, but such a one as the following. A familiar series expansion gives

$$\frac{1}{1+x^2}=1-x^2+x^4-x^6+ \cdot \cdot \cdot \cdot \cdot$$

The series on the right converges and is equal to the function on the left for all values between $x = -1$ and $x = +1$, not including these end-values, but diverges for all other real values of x. Yet these other values present no apparent peculiarity for the function $1/(1+x^2)$, which is continuous for every value of x. Let us, however, replace the real variable x by the complex variable z and use a well-known result in the theory of analytic functions of a complex variable. It is there shown that an analytic function $f(z)$ is representable by a power series

$$a_0+a_1z+a_2z^2+ \cdot \cdot \cdot \cdot ,$$

which converges at every point within and diverges at every point without a circle about the origin as center whose radius reaches to the nearest point at which the function fails to have a derivative, or is *singular*. Now the function $1/(1+z^2)$ becomes infinite for $z=\pm i$, or in (x, y) co-ordinates, for $x=0$, $y=\pm 1$. These points, and these only, are *singular points* for the function. Hence the series

$$1-z^2+z^4-z^6+ \cdot \cdot \cdot ,$$

which represents this function, must converge for all points within a circle about the origin passing through these points, and must diverge for every point outside that circle. In particular, when z has a real value x whose numerical value is greater than 1, the series must diverge.

We see then that the convergence or divergence of a series in the real variable x may be predicted and explained by using the theory of functions of a complex variable.

This example also illustrates a point of view in the theory of functions often associated with the name of the great mathematician Riemann, and perhaps first emphasized by him, in which the properties of a function and of associated series developments or other analytic representations are deduced from a minimum of definitions characterizing the *singularities* of the function. We see at once how necessary to the Riemannian program is the use of the complex variable.

With the introduction of the complex variable a host of applications was found in mathematical fields formerly studied through real functions. Faulty proofs were replaced by more satisfactory ones and a foundation for further progress was thus secured; new definite integrals were evaluated; a great light was thrown on the theory of the elliptic functions and of algebraic functions and their integrals in general; the theory of differential equations was marvelously developed.

But the study of functions of a complex variable has become essential to others beside the pure mathematician. The theory of maps is closely associated with it. The flow of electricity and the conduction of heat in two dimensions are investigated through this medium. To those who work with the applications of mathematics to other sciences, some knowledge of the theory of analytic functions of a complex variable has become indispensable.

3. **Founders of the theory.** Three great names have indelibly impressed themselves upon the history of the development of the theory of analytic functions, and even

upon its nomenclature. The first is that of the French mathematician Cauchy (1789–1857), who was not only a pioneer in this field, but who developed it far in certain directions. The other two names are those of the Germans Riemann (1826–66) and Weierstrass (1815–97). The following chapters may give an idea of some of their contributions.

CHAPTER II

COMPLEX NUMBERS

4. Elementary operations with complex numbers. When real numbers are combined by addition, subtraction, multiplication, or division with non-vanishing divisor, the results are real numbers; such numbers therefore form a *closed system* for these operations. But this is not always true when we pass to root extraction. No real number can be the square root of a negative real number.

The situation is analogous to one which exists for the number system composed of the positive integers. Here we have a system closed for addition, but in which subtraction of a number from one not greater than itself is impossible. When it seems desirable to allow such an operation, the difficulty is met by the enlargement of the number system so as to include zero and the negative integers. In order that division with non-vanishing divisor may always produce a number within the system, we pass from the system of positive and negative integers to the system of *rational* numbers which includes fractions as well as integers. The totality of all *real* numbers constitutes a still more inclusive system which is closed for the additional operation of passing to a finite limit.

We shall find that complex numbers include the real numbers and form a system which permits root extraction as well as the other operations we have noted. More than this, as we shall show later, every algebraic equation whose coefficients belong to the system of complex numbers has a solution which is a complex number. There are, of course, operations which are impossible in this system, as, for example, the solution of the equation $e^x = 0$, but those for which the system is closed include the entire set of the so-called *elementary operations*, a term which applies to addition, subtraction, multiplication, division with non-vanishing divisor, and root extraction, and this fact is a sufficient indication of the usefulness of complex numbers.

If we proceed in a purely formal way as in elementary algebra, it is natural to write a square root of a negative number, $-c$, as the product of $\sqrt{c}$ and $\sqrt{-1}$. The letter i is commonly used as a convenient substitute for the latter symbol. Thus the square root of a negative real number, $-b^2$, is written in the form ib, where b is real. We know, further, that every quadratic equation with real coefficients

$$x^2 + px + q = 0$$

is formally satisfied by expressions of the form $a + ib$ where a and b are real. Such *complex numbers* are added, subtracted, and multiplied according to the following rules in which we use the formulas of elementary algebra and the relation $i^2 = -1$ implied in our definition of the symbol i:

$$(a+ib)+(c+id) = (a\ +\ c)+i(b\ +\ d)\ ,$$
$$(a+ib)-(c+id) = (a\ -\ c)+i(b\ -\ d)\ ,$$
$$(a+ib)(c+id)\quad = (ac-bd)+i(ad+bc)\ .$$

Two complex numbers, $a + ib$ and $c + id$, are equal when and only when $a = c$ and $b = d$; their difference is then said to be zero. We call a the *real part* of $a+ib$; if b is zero, the complex number *is* the real number a. A complex number that is not real is *imaginary*, and an imaginary number whose real part is zero is a *pure imaginary*.

So much suffices to permit a proof, not given here, that every quadratic equation of the type indicated above has a complex number for a root. If this root, $a+ib$, is imaginary, then the *conjugate imaginary* $a+i(-b)$, or $a-ib$, is also a root. The sum and the product of two conjugate imaginaries are evidently real.

The quotient obtained by dividing $a+ib$ by a non-vanishing number $c+id$ is defined as the complex number $x+iy$ whose product with $c+id$ is equal to $a+ib$. This means that the equation

$$\frac{a+ib}{c+id}=x+iy$$

is regarded as equivalent to

$$(c+id)(x+iy)=a+ib \, .$$

From the definitions of multiplication and of equality, we obtain from this equation a pair of simultaneous linear equations for x and y whose solution gives

$$x+iy=\frac{a+ib}{c+id}=\frac{ac+bd}{c^2+d^2}+i\frac{bc-ad}{c^2+d^2} \, .$$

It is easy to verify the fact that the same result would have followed if we had multiplied both numerator and denominator of the fraction $(a+ib)/(c+id)$ by the conjugate of the denominator.

It would be natural next to define powers and roots of complex numbers, but at this point a geometric device becomes so useful that we turn to its consideration.

5. **Geometric representation.** Perhaps the most important step, certainly one of the first steps, in the development of the theory of complex numbers and functions consisted in noting that to each complex number $x+iy$ corresponds one and only one point (x, y) of a plane in which a system of rectangular co-ordinates has been set up. Thus plane geometry and complex numbers were brought into intimate contact. Although the idea had previously occurred to others, credit for its first detailed presentation belongs to Argand, whose pamphlet, *Essai sur une manière de représenter les quantités imaginaires dans les constructions géométriques*, bears the date 1806.

If the origin for the co-ordinate system is designated O, and if P is the point whose co-ordinates are (x, y), or more briefly the point (x, y), both the point P and the directed line or vector $\overline{OP}$ correspond uniquely to the complex number $x+iy$. We shall use both the point and the vector representation.

We now investigate the geometric interpretations of our formal algebraic definitions of addition, subtraction, multiplication, and division in terms of operations with vectors.

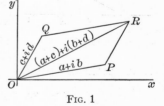

If, in Figure 1, the point P has the co-ordinates (a, b), and Q the co-ordinates (c, d), then these points, or the corresponding vectors $\overline{OP}$ and $\overline{OQ}$, represent the complex numbers $a+ib$ and $c+id$. The projection of $\overline{OP}$ on the *axis of reals Ox* is a, and on the *axis of pure imaginaries Oy* is b. If $\overline{PR}$ is drawn with the same direction and length as $\overline{OQ}$, then its projections on the axes will be c

Fig. 1

and d, respectively. The projections of $\overline{OR}$ are obviously $a+c$ and $b+d$; i.e., the vector $\overline{OR}$, or the point R, represents the number $(a+c)+i(b+d)$ which served to define the sum of $a+ib$ and $c+id$. This geometric method for addition is sometimes called the *parallelogram law*; it will be familiar to many readers as the way in which forces are compounded. It is, in fact, *vector addition*. The vector $\overline{OR}$ is called the sum of the vectors $\overline{OP}$ and $\overline{OQ}$.

If the sum of the vectors $\overline{OP}$ and $\overline{OQ}$ is $\overline{OR}$, as in Figure 1, then the vector difference $\overline{OR}-\overline{OP}$ is $\overline{OQ}$. To obtain $\overline{OQ}$ when $\overline{OR}$ and $\overline{OP}$ are given, we draw $\overline{PR}$ from the terminal point of $\overline{OP}$ to the terminal point of $\overline{OR}$. The vector $\overline{OQ}$ will then have the same length and direction as $\overline{PR}$. We have thus a geometrical equivalent for the *subtraction* of two complex numbers. Another formulation, which is left to the reader, would result from regarding the difference $(a+ib)-(c+id)$ as the sum of $a+ib$ and $-c-id$.

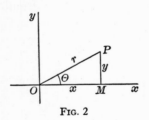

FIG. 2

The length and direction of a vector whose origin is at O enter explicitly in the definitions of polar co-ordinates. The familiar transformation from rectangular to polar co-ordinates, as indicated in Figure 2, gives

$$x=r\cos\theta, \qquad y=r\sin\theta,$$
$$r=\sqrt{x^2+y^2}, \qquad \theta=\tan^{-1}\frac{y}{x},$$
$$x+iy=r(\cos\theta+i\sin\theta).$$

Here the length of the radius vector, $r=\sqrt{x^2+y^2}$, is called the *modulus* or *absolute value* of $x+iy$, and is often written

$| x+iy |$, or if a single symbol z is used for $x+iy$, its absolute value is similarly written as $| z |$. The absolute value of a complex number is thus a real number which is never negative. Note that this includes the usual definition of the absolute value of a real number. The terms *angle, argument,* and *amplitude* are all used for the measure of the angle θ which corresponds to the direction of $\overline{OP}$. It is important to remember that while, for a given complex number other than zero, there is one and only one amplitude which is greater than or equal to zero and less than 2π, there is also one between 2π and 4π, one between 0 and -2π, and in fact an infinite number of others, of which any two differ by a multiple of 2π. Other values of $\tan^{-1} y/x$ correspond to the direction of $\overline{PO}$ and are discarded. The term "amplitude" may refer to a single angle θ, or to any one of the set $\theta+2k\pi$.

Using the polar representation, we obtain a formula for the product of two complex numbers $r_1(\cos \theta_1+i \sin \theta_1)$ and $r_2(\cos \theta_2+i \sin \theta_2)$ as follows:

$$r_1(\cos \theta_1+i \sin \theta_1) \cdot r_2(\cos \theta_2+i \sin \theta_2)$$
$$=r_1r_2[(\cos \theta_1 \cos \theta_2-\sin \theta_1 \sin \theta_2)+$$
$$i(\cos \theta_1 \sin \theta_2+\sin \theta_1 \cos \theta_2)]$$
$$=r_1r_2[\cos (\theta_1+\theta_2)+i \sin (\theta_1+\theta_2)] .$$

It thus appears that the *absolute value of the product is the product of the absolute values of the factors*, while *an amplitude of the product is a sum of amplitudes of the factors*. Note that from this rule it follows that the product of two complex numbers cannot vanish unless one of the factors vanishes, since a complex number is zero when and only when its absolute value is zero.

The product of more than two complex quantities can be obtained by multiplying the product of the first two by the third, then this product by the next, and so on. Obviously, the absolute value of the complete product will be the product of the absolute values of the factors, and any one of its amplitudes a sum of amplitudes of the factors. A special case is the formula

$$[r(\cos \theta + i \sin \theta)]^m = r^m(\cos m\theta + i \sin m\theta) ,$$

where m is a positive integer. When $r = 1$, this is called *De Moivre's theorem*.

Figure 3 suggests a geometric construction for the vector $\overline{OR}$ which corresponds to the product of the com-

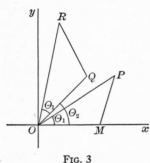

FIG. 3

plex numbers represented by $\overline{OP}$ and $\overline{OQ}$. Here $\overline{OM}$ is of unit length, and the triangle OQR is so constructed as to be similar to OMP, the angle QOR being equal to the angle xOP. Thus the angle xOR is equal, as it should be, to the sum of angles xOQ and xOP, and from the proportionality of corresponding sides we obtain the equations connecting the lengths OR, OP, and OQ of the vectors $\overline{OR}$, $\overline{OP}$, and $\overline{OQ}$,

$$\frac{OR}{OQ} = \frac{OP}{OM} = \frac{OP}{1} , \quad OR = OQ \cdot OP .$$

The latter of these equations corresponds to the one which should obtain for the absolute values of the corresponding complex numbers.

If we use the definition of division given on page 8, in which the quotient is determined as the number whose product with the divisor is equal to the dividend, it follows that for a non-vanishing divisor we have

$$\frac{r_1(\cos \theta_1 + i \sin \theta_1)}{r_2(\cos \theta_2 + i \sin \theta_2)} = \frac{r_1}{r_2}[\cos (\theta_1 - \theta_2) + i \sin (\theta_1 - \theta_2)] .$$

Thus the *absolute value of the quotient is the corresponding quotient of absolute values of dividend and divisor*, while *an amplitude of the quotient is obtained by subtracting an amplitude of the dividend from an amplitude of the divisor.* A geometric construction for the quotient follows from another interpretation of Figure 3, in which $\overline{OR}$ and $\overline{OQ}$, representing dividend and divisor, are first constructed, and $\overline{OP}$, representing the quotient, is taken so that triangle OMP is similar to triangle OQR.

A formula which is a special case under division is that for the reciprocal of a complex number. Since 1 is a complex number whose absolute value is unity and which has the amplitude zero, we have

$$\frac{1}{r(\cos \theta + i \sin \theta)} = \frac{1}{r}[\cos (0-\theta) + i \sin (0-\theta)] = \frac{1}{r}(\cos \theta - i \sin \theta) .$$

Hence the absolute value of the reciprocal of a complex number is the reciprocal of the absolute value of the number, while its amplitudes are negatives of the number's amplitudes.

6. **Root extraction.** We define an nth root of a complex number

$$z = r(\cos \theta + i \sin \theta)$$

to be a solution Z of the equation

$$Z^n = z .$$

If we write

$$Z = R(\cos \Theta + i \sin \Theta) ,$$

the foregoing equation becomes

$$R^n(\cos n\Theta + i \sin n\Theta) = r(\cos \theta + i \sin \theta) .$$

From the polar representation it is clear that two complex numbers are equal when and only when their absolute values are equal and their amplitude sets coincide. Hence we must have

$$R^n = r , \qquad n\Theta = \theta_1 + 2k\pi ,$$

where k is zero or a positive or negative integer and θ_1 is the least value of the amplitude of z that is not negative. This gives

$$R = r^{\frac{1}{n}} , \qquad \Theta = \frac{\theta_1}{n} + \frac{2k\pi}{n} ,$$

where $r^{\frac{1}{n}}$ denotes the positive real nth root of r. We may now write

$$Z = \sqrt[n]{z} = r^{\frac{1}{n}}\left[\cos\left(\frac{\theta_1}{n} + \frac{2k\pi}{n}\right) + i \sin\left(\frac{\theta_1}{n} + \frac{2k\pi}{n}\right) \right] .$$

By giving k the values $0, 1, 2, \ldots, n-1$, we obtain n different complex numbers, each of which is an nth root of z, but if we give any other positive or negative integral value to k the resulting amplitude will differ by a multiple of 2π from an amplitude of one of the roots already found, and the number thereby defined will be identical with that root. There are thus n and only n values for the nth root of any non-vanishing complex number. All have the same absolute value, given by the positive nth root of r, hence they are represented by points on a circle of this radius, while their amplitudes are such that these points divide the circle into n equal arcs. *The nth roots of z correspond to the vertices of a regular polygon of n sides inscribed in a circle about the origin whose radius is the positive nth root of r, one vertex having the amplitude θ_1/n.*

Of particular interest are the nth roots of unity, 1, ω_1, ω_2, ... , ω_{n-1}, given by the formula

$$\omega_k = \cos\frac{2k\pi}{n} + i\,\sin\frac{2k\pi}{n}\ .$$

The corresponding polygon is inscribed in the unit circle, with one vertex on the positive axis of reals. By De Moivre's formula,

$$\omega_k = \omega_1^k\ .$$

7. Summary; fundamental inequalities. We have shown above that the complex numbers form a closed system under the *elementary operations* of addition, subtraction, multiplication, division, and root extraction, and we have given geometric constructions corresponding to each of these operations.

It will be convenient to note here certain inequalities connected with sums and differences of complex numbers. For Figure 1, a familiar proposition of elementary geometry gives the following inequality for the lengths OR, OP, PR,

$$OR \leqq OP + PR\ .$$

In terms of the corresponding complex numbers we have

$$|\,(a+ib)+(c+id)\,| \leqq |\,a+ib\,| + |\,c+id\,|\ .$$

The reader will easily verify the following generalization: *The absolute value of a sum of complex numbers is never greater than the sum of their absolute values*. A special case is the relation

$$| a+ib | \leq | a | + | ib | = | a | + | b | .$$

Again, the proposition that the length of a side of a triangle is never less than the difference of the lengths of the other two sides gives the rule: *The absolute value of the difference of two complex numbers is never less than the absolute value of the difference of their absolute values*.

8. **References.** This chapter is purposely brief, because for most readers its subject matter is not new. Many college algebras have a chapter on complex numbers which includes practically all of the material here given. The treatment to be found in books on the theory of functions of a complex variable is often more complete and more suggestive. Out of the multitude of these treatises we select a few for frequent reference, not because they are superior to all others, but on account of their accessibility to American readers. They are, with one exception, comparatively recent publications by American houses. The exception is Osgood's *Lehrbuch der Funktionentheorie*, Volume I (2d ed., 1912, published by Teubner; 3d ed., 1920, a reprint of 2d ed.). Its comprehensive character, its careful accuracy, and its charm of style make impossible its omission from any list of references on the subject. We shall refer to it briefly as *Osgood*.

Two translations form part of our list. The first is Hedrick and Dunkel's rendering into English of Volume II, Part I, of Goursat's *Mathematical Analysis* (Ginn & Co., 1916), hereafter designated *Goursat-Hedrick*. The other, which we shall style *Burkhardt-Rasor*, is a translation by Rasor of Burkhardt's *Theory of Functions of a*

Complex Variable (D. C. Heath & Co., 1913). Both volumes, in original form, are parts of extended treatises covering the theory of real as well as complex variables. *Goursat-Hedrick* will be found somewhat concise. *Burkhardt-Rasor*, on the other hand, goes slowly and gives detailed treatments of fundamental questions, but does not carry the subject as far or give as many applications as most other texts.

Pierpont's *Functions of a Complex Variable* (Ginn & Co., 1914) is a more extended work, written in the author's interesting and individual style. It gives careful attention to foundations, but a distinguishing feature is the unusual amount of space (about half the book) given to applications of the general theory to transcendental functions, particularly the elliptic functions and those defined by homogeneous linear differential equations of the second order.

Townsend's *Functions of a Complex Variable* (Henry Holt & Co., 1915) presents an especially happy choice of topics for a first course. It does not go far in the discussion of special functions.

For questions involving analysis in general, using real as well as complex variables, we add to our list Wilson's *Advanced Calculus* (Ginn & Co., 1912). It is usually concise, always careful in its statements, and a veritable compendium in its field.

The material of this chapter is treated briefly by *Osgood, Goursat-Hedrick*, and *Wilson*. *Burkhardt-Rasor* and *Pierpont* give, perhaps, the most detail. Page references follow: *Osgood*, pages, 202–10; *Goursat-Hedrick*, pages 3–6, 14; *Burkhardt-Rasor*, pages 1–27; *Pierpont*, pages 1–24; *Townsend*, pages 1–19; *Wilson*, pages 153–56.

CHAPTER III

REAL FUNCTIONS OF REAL VARIABLES

9. Functions of a real variable. Before we take up functions of a complex variable we must consider some of the fundamental properties of functions of real variables. It is assumed that the reader has a knowledge of the calculus which will enable us to abbreviate the discussion in places.

According to the definition of Dirichlet (1805–59), a *dependent variable y* is a function of an *independent variable x* if to each value of x there corresponds one or more values for y. When this relation is expressed in the form of an equation in mathematical notation, the function is *explicit* if the equation is of the form $y = f(x)$, and is *implicit* if the equation is of the form $f(x, y) = 0$. Examples of explicit functions are *polynomials*,

$$y = a_0 x^n + a_1 x^{n-1} + \cdots + a_n ;$$

rational functions, in which y is the quotient of two polynomials; and the *power function* $y = x^r$, where r is any real number. *Algebraic functions* are implicitly given by equations of form $f(x, y) = 0$ in which the function $f(x, y)$ is a polynomial in y as well as in x; it can be shown that they include polynomials and rational functions as well as many power functions. Functions that are not algebraic are *transcendental*; familiar examples are $y = e^x$, where e is the natural base of logarithms; $y = \log x$; the trigonometric functions $y = \sin x$, $y = \cos x$; and inverse trigonometric functions such as $y = \sin^{-1} x$.

10. Limits. If x takes on in succession an infinite sequence of values x_1, x_2, x_3, ... , we say the variable x has the limit X on the sequence, or that the sequence has the limit X, if the numerical difference $\mid x_n - X \mid$ becomes and remains, as n increases, less than any positive number, no matter how small. This does not mean that each x_n is necessarily nearer X than its predecessor, but it does mean that if we start at a place sufficiently far along in the sequence, then each subsequent term will differ numerically from X by less than $1/10$, for example; if we go enough farther, then each subsequent term will differ from X by less than $1/100$; and so on indefinitely. Geometrically, if we represent the values of x by points on the x-axis, these points cluster about X in such a way that if we start at a place far enough along in the sequence, all subsequent terms lie in the interval $[X - 1/10,\ X + 1/10]$; or we can start far enough along so that all subsequent terms will lie in the interval $[X - 1/100,\ X + 1/100]$; and so on. But this particular type of successive fencing in around X is not essential. The definition contained in the opening sentence of the paragraph, when more precisely worded, states that no matter what positive number ϵ, small or large, is proposed, an integer m exists for that ϵ such that all the terms of the sequence beginning with the mth lie in the interval $[X - \epsilon,\ X + \epsilon]$; or, in mathematical notation,

$$\mid x_n - X \mid < \epsilon ,\ \text{for all } n \geqq m .$$

A particular set of ϵ's approaching zero, like $1/10$, $1/100$, ... , may assist our intuitions, but logically it does not belong in the definition.

We say that x *becomes infinite* on a sequence if for every number M, no matter how large, there exists a place in the sequence beyond which all terms numerically exceed M.

If $y = f(x)$ is defined for all values of x in an interval $[a, b]$ except, possibly, for the one value $x = X$, and is *single-valued* (i.e., each value of x gives but one value of y), then a sequence of values $y_1, y_2, \ldots$, of the function corresponds to each sequence $x_1, x_2, \ldots$, whose terms are in $[a, b]$ and of which X is not a member. Now let us consider all possible x sequences in $[a, b]$ which do not include X but have X as their common limit. If the corresponding y sequences all have a common limit Y, then we say that y, or $f(x)$, approaches the limit Y as x approaches X, and write this in abbreviated form,

$$(1) \qquad \lim_{x = X} f(x) = Y .$$

Geometrically, the x and y sequences of the preceding paragraphs taken together define *sequences of points* P_1,

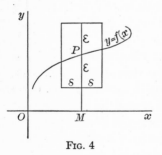

FIG. 4

$P_2, \ldots$, whose co-ordinates are (x_1, y_1), (x_2, y_2), $\ldots$ We are requiring that when the abscissas of these points approach a limit $OM = X$, the ordinates approach a limit $MP = Y$. We then say that the sequence of points $P_1, P_2, \ldots$, has the point P, whose co-ordinates are (X, Y), as a *limit point*. This is the case, for example, when the graph of $y = f(x)$ is an ordinary smooth curve as in Figure 4. But even if the graph is of a less simple type all such sequences will surely have P as a limit point

if there is a sequence of rectangles of which a typical member is shown in Figure 4, closing down to P, each containing all the points on $y=f(x)$ whose abscissas are within its projection on Ox. However, the use of a particular sequence of rectangles is open to the same objection here as was that of a sequence of intervals in defining the limit of x. It will suffice if for each width 2ϵ that may be proposed there exists a rectangle of the sort shown in Figure 4 such that all points on $y=f(x)$ between its vertical sides produced are within the rectangle; in other words, no matter what positive constant ϵ is proposed, a δ may be found, so that for every x differing numerically from X by less than δ the corresponding y differs numerically from Y by less than ϵ:

(2) $|y-Y|<\epsilon$ for all x such that $0<|x-X|<\delta$.

If this is true, then the function $f(x)$ must have a limit by our every sequence definition, for in any sequence $y_1, y_2, \ldots, y_n, \ldots$, we shall have $|y_n-Y|<\epsilon$ for all $n \geqq m$ if only m is so large that $|x_n-X|<\delta$ for all $n \geqq m$.

But the question arises as to whether formula (2) is completely equivalent to our first definition of the limit expressed in formula (1), so that it can be taken as an alternative definition. The answer will be affirmative if (2) *must* be satisfied whenever (1) holds according to the sequence definition. We shall not give a proof here, but as a matter of fact *the two definitions are identical in scope*.

A definition which should be compared with the one given above in which x becomes infinite on a sequence states that $f(x)$ is said to *become infinite* as x approaches

X if, no matter what positive constant M is assigned, we have $|f(x)| > M$ for all values of x sufficiently near X, the latter value not included. This can be expressed more formally. There are variations of this definition to suit cases where x itself becomes infinite, and others where we distinguish *positively infinite* from *negatively infinite*, which we need not state explicitly here.

11. **Continuous functions.** We now consider a function $y = f(x)$ which may or may not be defined for $x = X$ but is single-valued for all other values of x in an interval $[a, b]$ to which $x = X$ is interior. The function $y = f(x)$ is continuous at $x = X$ if and only if the following three conditions hold: (1) $f(x)$ has a single value for $x = X$; (2) $f(x)$ has a limit Y as x approaches X; (3) $Y = f(X)$. Geometrically, the graph of the function is unbroken at the point (X, Y). If the function is continuous for every value of x in $[a, b]$ it is said to be *continuous throughout the interval* $[a, b]$. If $[a, b]$ does not include its end-points $x = a$ and $x = b$, it is said to be an *open* interval, but if it does include both, then it is a *closed* interval. If $[a, b]$ is closed, a function $f(x)$ continuous throughout $[a, b]$ is understood to have the limits $f(a)$ and $f(b)$ for all sequences of points of $[a, b]$ that approach a and b, respectively.

Examples of functions discontinuous at $x = 0$ are $f(x) = 1/x$, which becomes infinite; $f(x) = \sin 1/x$, which has an infinite number of finite oscillations; and the function $f(x)$ which is defined so as to equal 0 to the left of the origin and 1 to the right. Note that a function would be discontinuous if it were simply not defined for $x = X$, even if it were continuous at every point near X and had a limit as x approached X on every sequence not including X as a member. In the examples just given, the functions are not defined for $x=0$, and for this additional reason are discontinuous there.

Sums and products of continuous functions are continuous, and the same is true for quotients with non-vanishing denominators. Continuous functions have certain important properties, proofs for which may be found in the standard works on functions of real or complex variables. For example, if a function is single-valued and continuous throughout a closed interval it has finite greatest and least values there. Further, a function continuous throughout a closed interval is *uniformly continuous* there. This means that in the ϵ, δ definition of a limit, if any ϵ has been proposed, a corresponding δ can be found which will apply not merely for one value X, but for all values of X in $[a, b]$ simultaneously. The corresponding ϵ, δ rectangle (see Fig. 4) of constant dimensions will, if moved parallel to itself with its midpoint P on the graph of $y=f(x)$, never be cut through its top or bottom by the curve.

12. **Derivatives and integrals.** A more restricted class of functions is composed of those which have derivatives. We recall the familiar definition for $f'(x_0)$, the derivative of $f(x)$ at x_0, given by the formula

$$\lim_{\Delta x = 0} \frac{f(x_0 + \Delta x) - f(x_0)}{\Delta x} = f'(x_0) .$$

When x_0 is allowed to vary, $f'(x_0)$ is called the *derived function*, or more briefly, the *derivative*. If Δx is restricted to positive values in the expression whose limit defines the derivative, this limit is called the *derivative on the right*, and similarly for the *derivative on the left*. A function which has a derivative at a point must be continuous there, but the converse is not necessarily true.

It may be useful to recall also the notions of the indefinite and definite integrals as they occur in the calculus. An indefinite integral of $f(x)$ is usually first defined as a function whose derivative is $f(x)$, and is later expressed in terms of the definite integral with variable upper limit of integration. We shall follow this procedure here.

The definite integral from $x = a$ to $x = b$ of a function $f(x)$ is defined by means of the formula

$$(3) \quad \int_a^b f(x)\ dx = \lim_{\Delta x = 0} [f(x_1)\Delta x_1 + f(x_2)\Delta x_2 + \cdots + f(x_n)\Delta x_n]$$

$$= \lim_{\Delta x = 0} \sum_{i=1}^{n} f(x_i)\Delta x_i.$$

Here the notation indicates that the interval $[a, b]$ has been divided into n successive parts of lengths Δx_1, Δx_2, ... , Δx_n, and the points $x_1, x_2, \ldots, x_n$ have been chosen arbitrarily in the respective subdivisions corresponding to the subscripts. We still need to explain what we mean by the limit as Δx approaches zero of the sum in brackets on the right side of formula (3). Let us designate this sum by the symbol S_n. We are to think of a sum S_{n_1} corresponding to a division of $[a, b]$ into n_1 parts and in which the maximum length of a subdivision is δ_1, then of a new sum S_{n_2} corresponding to n_2 subdivisions with maximum subdivision length δ_2, and so on. In the infinite sequence S_{n_1}, S_{n_2}, ... , the lower subscript becomes infinite, while δ approaches zero. At the end of this chapter will be found references to satisfactory proofs that if $f(x)$ is continuous throughout the closed interval [a , b], *every* sequence of *S*'s formed as indicated will have the same limit, which we term the *definite integral from a to b of f(x)*. The property of uniform continuity plays an important part in these proofs.

In order that the limits of integration may be any numbers whatever we make the conventions that the integral from *b* to *a* is the negative of the integral from *a* to *b*, and that the integral from *a* to *a* is zero.

Properties immediately deducible from our definition when $f(x)$ is continuous are expressed by the formulas:

$$\int_a^b f(x)dx + \int_b^c f(x)dx = \int_a^c f(x)dx \; ;$$

$$\int_a^b f(x)dx > \int_a^b \phi(x)dx \; ,$$

if $f(x) \geqq \phi(x)$ throughout [a , b], and $f(x) > \phi(x)$ throughout some subinterval of [a , b]; and the *special mean value theorem for integrals*

$$\int_a^b f(x)dx = f(\xi)(b-a) \; , \qquad a < \xi < b \; .$$

If *b* is now replaced by the variable *x*, or better by *X* in order to avoid confusion with the *variable of integration x*, the definite integral becomes a function of its upper limit, and we write

$$F(X) = \int_a^X f(x)dx \; .$$

With the aid of the special mean value theorem, it can be shown that the derivative of $F(X)$ is $f(X)$, and the indefinite integral is identified as the expression $F(x)+c$, where *c* is any constant.

The reader will recall the geometrical interpretations of the derivative as the slope of the tangent, and of the integral as an area.

With suitable modifications the definition of the integral has been extended so as to apply to discontinuous functions. A discussion of this subject will be found in works on the calculus, usually under the title "Improper Integrals," but is not essential for the reading of this monograph.

13. Functions of two variables. We shall here give definitions that apply to functions of two variables. The reader can often easily make for himself extensions to functions of more variables, or can find them in the references given at the close of the chapter.

As functions of one variable are defined on an interval, so functions of two variables are defined for each point of a *region*. This term applies to a single piece of a plane. If a region includes its boundary it is *closed*, if not it is *open*. We shall not here attempt to be precise regarding the nature of the boundary. By a *neighborhood* of a point we mean a region to which the point is interior.

On page 20 we have stated as a definition that a sequence of points (x_1, y_1), (x_2, y_2), ... , approaches a limit (X, Y) if the sequence x_1, x_2, ... , approaches X as a limit and y_1, y_2, ... , approaches Y. An equivalent definition states that if (X, Y) is made the center of any square whose sides, of arbitrary length 2δ, are parallel to the co-ordinate axes, then there is always a place in the sequence beyond which all points of the sequence lie in the square. A circle, or other suitable neighborhood of (X, Y), could replace the square.

This leads to definitions of the limit of a function of

two variables analogous to those which hold for functions of a single variable. Thus $f(x, y)$, defined and single-valued in a region T, except possibly at the point (X, Y), is said to approach a limit Z when x and y, as independent variables, approach X and Y, provided that for every sequence (x_1, y_1), (x_2, y_2), ... , of points of T which approaches the limit (X, Y), but of which (X, Y) is not a member, the sequence $f(x_1, y_1)$, $f(x_2, y_2)$, ... , approaches Z. When this is true it is expressed by the formula

$$\lim_{x=X,\, y=Y} f(x, y) = Z .$$

If we consider only all such sequences of points as lie on a continuous curve through (X, Y), the statements above define approach to the limit Z *along this curve*; of course x and y cannot both be regarded as independent variables in this case. On the other hand, we have the ϵ, δ definition of the limit where x and y are independent, which requires that for every positive number ϵ that may be proposed a positive number δ can be found such that for all points (x, y) in the square shown in Figure 5, except possibly (X, Y), the value

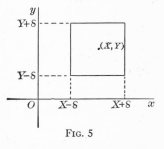

FIG. 5

of $f(x, y)$ differs numerically from Z by less than ϵ. These two definitions are equivalent.

A function $f(x, y)$, defined and single valued throughout a region including the point (X, Y), is *continuous* there if

$$\lim_{x=X,\, y=Y} f(x, y) = f(X, Y) .$$

Note that the limit $f(X, Y)$ must be approached along *every* continuous curve through (X, Y). A function continuous at every point of a region is said to be continuous throughout the region.

If we take the derivative of $f(x, y)$ with respect to x, as though y were a constant, we obtain the *first partial derivative with respect to* x, written $\partial f/\partial x$; similarly for $\partial f/\partial y$. *Partial derivatives of second order* are defined as follows:

$$\frac{\partial^2 f}{\partial x^2}=\frac{\partial}{\partial x}\left(\frac{\partial f}{\partial x}\right), \qquad \frac{\partial^2 f}{\partial x \partial y}=\frac{\partial}{\partial x}\left(\frac{\partial f}{\partial y}\right), \qquad \frac{\partial^2 f}{\partial y^2}=\frac{\partial}{\partial y}\left(\frac{\partial f}{\partial y}\right),$$

and similarly for partial derivatives of higher orders. A useful formula for functions with continuous first partial derivatives connects the increment Δu of a function $u=f(x, y)$ with the increments of x and y. We define Δu by the equation

$$\Delta u=f(x+\Delta x, y+\Delta y)-f(x, y).$$

A familiar device (for references, see the end of this chapter) expresses Δu in the form

$$(4) \qquad \Delta u=\frac{\partial f}{\partial x}\Delta x+\frac{\partial f}{\partial y}\Delta y+\epsilon_1\Delta x+\epsilon_2\Delta y,$$

where ϵ_1 and ϵ_2 are functions of x, y, Δx, and Δy which approach zero when Δx and Δy, as independent variables, approach zero. This result will be found useful in discussing the derivative of a function of a complex variable.

14. **Double integrals.** In defining the definite integral of a function of x only, we divided a segment of the x-axis

into subintervals of lengths Δx_1, Δx_2, ... , Δx_n, and considered the limit of a sequence of sums of the type $\sum_{i=1}^{n} f(x_i)\Delta x_i$. The *double integral* is a generalization to two dimensions. We divide a region A into subregions of areas ΔA_1, ΔA_2, ... , ΔA_n, and by (ξ_i, n_i) we designate a point of the ith subregion chosen according to some scheme. We then form the sum $\sum_{i=1}^{n} f(\xi_i, n_i)\Delta A_i$, and consider sequences of sums of this type in which n becomes infinite and the maximum diameter of the subregions approaches zero. If the limit of every such sequence exists and this limit is the same for all such sequences, it is called the double integral of $f(x, y)$ over the region A, and is written

$$\iint_A f(x, y)dA .$$

By dividing the x-axis into intervals of lengths Δx_i, and the y-axis similarly, and drawing perpendiculars at the points of subdivision, the region A is divided into rectangles of area $\Delta x_i \Delta y_j$, and pieces of such rectangles. But it can be shown that in case the boundary of A is not too complicated a curve, the limit of the sequences of sums in our definition would be the same if the non-rectangular subregions were neglected. The sums, then, can be replaced by *double sums* whose typical term is of form $f(x_i, y_j) \Delta x_i \Delta y_j$, and for this reason the double integral is written

$$\iint_A f(x, y)dx\, dy .$$

In case the boundary of A is of the familiar convex sort that is met in but two points by a parallel to either co-ordinate axis, a natural way to sum the expressions $f(x_i, y_j)\Delta x_i\Delta y_j$ is to add up those that correspond to the

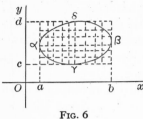

FIG. 6

rectangles in the first row of Figure 6, then those for the next row, and so on, then to add these row-sums. Let us write down a typical row-sum; a glance at Figure 6 shows that the first rectangle in the ith row will, in general, come in some other *column* than the first, say the rth, and the last in the sth. Our row-sum, then, has the form

$$f(x_r, y_j)\Delta x_r\Delta y_j + f(x_{r+1}, y_j)\Delta x_{r+1}\Delta y_j + \cdots \cdots$$
$$+ f(x_s, y_j)\Delta x_s\Delta y_j.$$

But, if we take out the factor Δy_j, this is exactly such a sum as we would use in defining the integral from $x = x_r$ to $x = x_{s+1}$ of $f(x, y_j)$. Here x_r and x_{s+1} are approximately the points in which the boundary curve is cut by the line $y = y_j$. If the equation of the left-hand part $\gamma\alpha\delta$ of the boundary curve is $x = \phi_1(y)$, and that of $\gamma\beta\delta$ is $x = \phi_2(y)$ our typical row-sum is approximately

$$F(y_j)\Delta y_j = \left[\int_{\phi_1(y_j)}^{\phi_2(y_j)} f(x, y_j)dx \right] \Delta y_j.$$

The sum of these row-sums at once suggests the integral

$$\int_c^d F(y)dy,$$

or the *iterated integral*

$$\int_c^d \left[\int_{\phi_1(y)}^{\phi_2(y)} f(x, y)dx \right] dy ,$$

which is often written without the brackets. Here c and d are the least and greatest values of y in A.

The reader will understand that we are not attempting a logically complete proof of this reduction of a double integral to the foregoing iterated integral such as may be found in standard works on advanced calculus or theory of functions of real variables. But if we grant the correctness of the reduction indicated, it is clear that the double integral is also equal to the iterated integral

$$\int_a^b \int_{\psi_1(x)}^{\psi_2(x)} f(x, y)dy\, dx ,$$

where $y = \psi_1(x)$ is the equation of $\alpha\gamma\beta$, and $y = \psi_2(x)$ that of $\alpha\delta\beta$, while a and b are the least and greatest values of x in A.

If the region A is not of the convex sort we have just discussed, we may express the double integral over A as the sum of double integrals over suitable subdivisions of A.

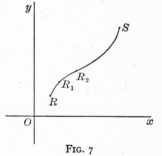

Fig. 7

15. **Curve integrals.** Another extension of ordinary integration leads to *curve integrals*. Instead of a segment of the x-axis, the field of integration is a piece of a continuous curve C, from a point R to a point S (Fig. 7). If C is a closed curve, R coincides with S. On the curve segment C, if both x and y increase as we go from

R to S, we take points of division R_1, R_2, ... , dividing it into n subsegments of lengths Δs_1, Δs_2, ... , Δs_n, whose projections on the x-axis are of lengths Δx_1, Δx_2, ... , Δx_n; and on the y-axis Δy_1, Δy_2, ... , Δy_n. The function to be integrated being $f(x, y)$, we take a point (x_1, y_1) on the first subsegment, a point (x_2, y_2) on the second, and so on, and form the sums

$$f(x_1, y_1)\Delta s_1 + f(x_2, y_2)\Delta s_2 + \cdots + f(x_n, y_n)\Delta s_n,$$
$$f(x_1, y_1)\Delta x_1 + f(x_2, y_2)\Delta x_2 + \cdots + f(x_n, y_n)\Delta x_n,$$
$$f(x_1, y_1)\Delta y_1 + f(x_2, y_2)\Delta y_2 + \cdots + f(x_n, y_n)\Delta y_n.$$

If the function and curve are of an ordinary sort, all sequences of sums of any one of these kinds, in which n becomes infinite and the length of the maximum subsegment approaches zero, have a common limit. These limits we define as the curve integrals

$$\int_C f(x, y)ds, \qquad \int_C f(x, y)dx, \qquad \int_C f(x, y)dy.$$

We often indicate under a single sign of integration the sum of two curve integrals, and exhibit the co-ordinates of the end-points thus:

$$\int_{C}{}_{(a, b)}^{(c, d)} P(x, y)dx + Q(x, y)dy.$$

If C is composed of successive segments C_1, C_2, ... , the integral over C is equal to the sum of the integrals over C_1, C_2, ... We also agree that the integral over C from R to S is the negative of the integral over C in the opposite sense from S to R. These conventions enable us to extend our definitions of curve integrals to cover cases where either x, or y, or both, do not always increase as we go from R to S.

If C has the equation $y = F(x)$, where $F(x)$ is single-valued and continuous, we easily change the curve integral with respect to x into an ordinary one by the formula

$$\int_{C\,(a,\,b)}^{(c,\,d)} P(x,y)dx = \int_a^c P[x,F(x)]dx .$$

This follows from the equality of the sums which can be used in defining each of the foregoing integrals, since $y_i = F(x_i)$. We may similarly express a curve integral with respect to y if C has an equation $x = \Phi(y)$, where $\Phi(y)$ is single-valued; and by dividing C into segments of the required kind, if C itself is not of this sort, we may express the integral over C as a sum of ordinary integrals. If the curve is given by parametric equations $x = f(t)$, $y = \phi(t)$, the substitution of the functions for x and y, and of their differentials for dx and dy, changes a curve integral with respect to x and y into an ordinary one with respect to t.

As an example, let us evaluate

$$\int_{C\,(0,\,0)}^{(1,\,1)} (x^2 - y^2)dx - 2xy\ dy ,$$

where C is the broken line OMS of Figure 8. The integral along C is the sum of the integral along OM and the integral along MS. The equation of OM is $y = 0$, and the substitution of $y = 0$, $dy = 0$ in the foregoing integral

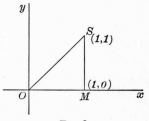

Fig. 8

along OM leaves us

$$\int_0^1 x^2 dx = 1/3.$$

Along MS we have $x = 1$, and consequently $dx = 0$, so that our integral along this line reduces to

$$-\int_0^1 2y \, dy = -1.$$

Adding these results, we obtain $-2/3$ as the value of the integral along C. If we used the straight line OS as our curve C, we should have $y = x$, $dy = dx$, and the integral would reduce to

$$-\int_0^1 2x^2 dx = -2/3,$$

as before. In fact, with this integrand the integral along any curve of an ordinary sort from O to S would have the same value, $-2/3$, but if, for example, the term $-2xy \, dy$ were replaced by $xy \, dy$, the value of the resulting integral would depend upon the path as well as upon the integrand and the end-points, as one may readily verify.

16. **Green's lemma.** We have seen that both a double integral over a region and a curve integral around its boundary can be expressed in terms of ordinary integrals. Cannot we then express a double integral over the region bounded by a closed curve C as a curve integral around C. Let us turn back to Figure 6 and our reduction of the double integral to an iterated integral for the sort of boundary there considered, and let us express our integrand $f(x, y)$ in the form $\partial Q(x, y)/\partial x$. We have

$$\iint_A \frac{\partial}{\partial x} Q(x, y) dx\, dy = \int_c^d \left[\int_{\phi_1(y)}^{\phi_2(y)} \frac{\partial}{\partial x} Q(x, y) dx \right] dy$$

$$= \int_c^d \left[Q(\phi_2(y), y) - Q(\phi_1(y), y) \right] dy$$

$$= \int_c^d Q(\phi_2(y), y) dy - \int_c^d Q(\phi_1(y), y) dy .$$

Now of these last two integrals the first is at once identified as the curve integral along $\gamma\beta\delta$ of $Q(x, y)$ with respect to y and the latter as the corresponding curve integral along $\gamma\alpha\delta$. The negative of the latter is the curve integral along $\delta\alpha\gamma$, so that

$$\iint_A \frac{\partial Q}{\partial x} dx\, dy = \int_{\gamma\beta\delta} Q dy + \int_{\delta\alpha\gamma} Q dy = \int_C Q dy .$$

If our integrand had been $\partial P/\partial y$ and we had integrated first with respect to y, then x, we would have had

$$\iint_A \frac{\partial P}{\partial y} dy\, dx = \int_{\alpha\delta\beta} P dx + \int_{\beta\gamma\alpha} P dx = - \int_C P dx .$$

The negative sign here is due to the fact that we are going around C in an opposite sense to the one taken for the curve integral of Q with respect to y. We shall take the *positive* sense about C as that which leaves the region A to the left.

Taken together, these results give us what is often styled *Green's theorem* but is more correctly called *Green's lemma*, since it was assumed rather than proved in Green's celebrated paper on mathematical physics (1828). It is expressed by the formula

$$\int_C P dx + Q dy = \iint_A \left(\frac{\partial Q}{\partial x} - \frac{\partial P}{\partial y} \right) dx\, dy .$$

Without going into further details, we remark that this formula holds even when C is met in more than two points by a parallel to a co-ordinate axis, and when A is a region in which holes have been punched. In this last case the curve integral is to be taken around each boundary curve in a sense that leaves A to the left.

17. Integrals independent of the path. Curve integrals have many applications in mathematical physics and elsewhere, but our interest here is in their application to functions of a complex variable. In this connection we find that integrals whose value does not depend upon the curve along which we integrate are of especial importance. In Figure 9 the two curves C_1 and C_2 from (a, b) to (c, d) are such that C_1 taken forward and C_2 taken backward form a single closed curve C in the positive sense, inclosing an area A. To require the integral of $Pdx+Qdy$ along C_1 to be equal to its integral along C_2 is the same as requiring the integral forward along C_1 plus the integral backward on C_2 to be zero. That is, an equivalent formulation is

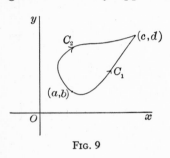

FIG. 9

$$\int_C Pdx+Qdy=0 .$$

A glance at the equation that expresses Green's lemma shows that *if $\partial Q/\partial x = \partial P/\partial y$ identically throughout A, the curve integral around C will be zero.* If this identity exists throughout a region T_1 whose boundary is a single closed curve that does not cut itself, and to which (a, b) and (c, d) are interior, then the integral from (a, b) to (c, d) will be the same for any two curves with common end-points, such as C_1 and C_2, which lie wholly within T_1. Even if C_1 and C_2 intersect a finite number of times, and under less restrictive conditions also, this result is still true and the integral is said to be independent of the path of integration. When this is the case, we frequently omit C as part of the symbol of integration. The argument is reversible; P and Q being functions with continuous first partial derivatives, we *must* have $\partial Q/\partial x = \partial P/\partial y$ identically throughout T_1 if the value of

$$\int_C Pdx + Qdy$$

is to be the same for all paths in T_1 with common end-points.

If (c, d) is replaced by a variable point (X, Y), an integral independent of the path becomes a function of X and Y. Let us write

$$F(X, Y) = \int_{(a, b)}^{(X, Y)} P(x, y)dx + Q(x, y)dy .$$

We can easily show that

$$\frac{\partial F}{\partial X} = P(X, Y) , \qquad \frac{\partial F}{\partial Y} = Q(X, Y) .$$

To obtain the former of these results, choose as the path of integration the "elbow path" composed of a parallel to the y-axis from (a, b) to (a, Y) followed by the perpendicular line from (a, Y) to (X, Y). On the first of these lines we have $x=a$, $dx=0$; and on the second, $y=Y$, $dy=0$. Hence

$$F(X,\,Y)=\int_b^Y Q(a,\,y)dy+\int_a^X P(x,\,Y)dx\;.$$

The first of these integrals is not a function of X, hence its derivative with respect to X is zero, and from our discussion, on page 25, of the derivative of an ordinary integral, it follows that the derivative with respect to X of the second integral is $P(X,\,Y)$. Thus this last expression is the partial derivative of $F(X,\,Y)$ with respect to X. The other elbow path can be used in evaluating $\partial F/\partial Y$. The objection that an elbow path might get us outside the region of definition of P and Q is met by taking as part of our path any curve in T_1 that joins $(a,\,b)$ to a point $(\alpha,\,\beta)$ from which elbow paths to $(X,\,Y)$ lie in T_1.

18. **Implicit functions.** Elementary works on the calculus give formulas for the derivative of a function defined implicitly by an equation $f(x,y)=0$, but seldom even refer to the problem of determining whether a given equation of this kind has a real solution y for every value of x, or whether there is one or more than one value of y for each x. If we follow formulas blindly we conclude that when our equation is $x^2+y^2=0$, the derivative of y with respect to x is $-x/y$; an absurd result if x and y are to be real, since the equation is satisfied in real numbers only by $x=0$, $y=0$.

Suppose, then, we first examine the relatively simple equation $x=\phi(y)$, where $\phi(y)$ is single-valued and has a continuous derivative throughout an interval $c<y<d$. Let y_0 designate a value of y in this interval, and x_0 the

corresponding value of x. When will the equation have a solution of the form $y = F(x)$, where $F(x)$ is real and single-valued in some interval $[a, b]$ to which x_0 is interior and such that $y_0 = F(x_0)$? When will this function be continuous? A simple answer is that both these requirements will be met if the derived function $\phi'(y)$ is not zero when $y = y_0$. A point for which $\phi'(y)$ vanishes, as P or Q in Fig. 10, may be a turning-point for the curve $x = \phi(y)$. At a point

like (x_0, y_0) the curve is of the ordinary sort whose equation is $y = F(x)$. Let us note that there may be another solution $y = F_1(x)$, corresponding to the curve segment PQ, but we would not have $y_0 = F_1(x_0)$. From this point in our argument we may discuss the deriva-

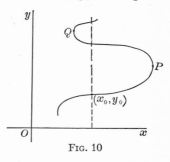

Fig. 10

tive of y as in elementary calculus and obtain the formula $F'(x) = 1/\phi'(y)$.

A corresponding condition, if the equation has **the** form $f(x, y) = 0$ and $f(x, y)$ has continuous first partial derivatives in a neighborhood of a particular solution point (x_0, y_0), is that $\partial f/\partial y$ be not zero at (x_0, y_0). There is then one and only one solution $y = F(x)$ passing through (x_0, y_0) which is single-valued and continuous throughout an interval about $x = x_0$.

It may be noted that $x^2 + y^2 = 0$, whose only real solution is given by the point $(0, 0)$, does not meet the condition $\partial f/\partial y \neq 0$ at the origin and hence does not come under our theorem. Another example where the condition fails at the origin is given by $x^2 - y^2 = 0$, its solution being the function $y = \pm x$ which is *double-valued* in every neighborhood of the origin. As to the condition $\partial f/\partial y \neq 0$, it will be recalled that the formula for dy/dx is

$$\frac{dy}{dx} = -\frac{\dfrac{\partial f}{\partial x}}{\dfrac{\partial f}{\partial y}},$$

so that the vanishing of $\partial f/\partial y$ might well be expected to have some significance.

In the next chapter we shall find that a similar question regarding functions of a complex variable is reducible to the consideration of real solutions of a pair of simultaneous equations $u = f_1(x, y)$, $v = f_2(x, y)$ where f_1 and f_2 are single-valued and have continuous first partial derivatives throughout a neighborhood of a point (x_0, y_0) to which corresponds (u_0, v_0). The formulas for the partial derivatives of x and y with respect to u and v have the *Jacobian* determinant

$$\begin{vmatrix} \dfrac{\partial f_1}{\partial x} & \dfrac{\partial f_1}{\partial y} \\[2ex] \dfrac{\partial f_2}{\partial x} & \dfrac{\partial f_2}{\partial y} \end{vmatrix}$$

in their denominators. It is this determinant whose non-vanishing at (x_0, y_0) insures the existence of unique solutions $x = F_1(u, v)$, $y = F_2(u, v)$, satisfied by u_0, v_0, x_0, y_0, and such that F_1 and F_2 are single-valued and continuous throughout a neighborhood of (u_0, v_0).

19. **References.** In the works cited at the end of the previous chapter, portions especially devoted to topics discussed in the present chapter are as follows: *Osgood*,

Chapters I, II, and IV; *Burkhardt-Rasor*, Chapter III; *Pierpont*, Chapter V; *Wilson*, Chapters I, II, IV, V, XI, XII. *Townsend* separates as little as possible the theory of functions of real variables from that of functions of complex variables, while *Goursat-Hedrick* relegates real variables to Volume I, which is almost indispensable to one who wishes to gain a thorough knowledge of the advanced calculus and an introduction to the theory of functions of real variables.

In *Osgood* will be found a systematic and in places an extended and critical treatment. Chapters III and V supplement the ones mentioned above. Some of the more difficult parts of Chapters IV and V are perhaps best omitted at a first reading.

Burkhardt-Rasor is briefer and presupposes some knowledge of the volume which precedes it in the German edition. *Pierpont* also does not go deeply into the subject, but its discussion of certain points should prove both interesting and instructive to the beginner in this field.

In *Wilson* the discussion is fuller in many places than in the other references here given. In Chapters I and II will be found a review of elementary calculus and a useful formulation of fundamental ideas about limits and continuity. The other chapters are on more special subjects.

We add a few particular references which supply illustrations or proofs omitted or left incomplete in this chapter.

For a proof that our two definitions for the limit of a function are equivalent, the reader will need to consult a reference outside our list. He will find such a proof in Pierpont's *The Theory of Functions of Real Variables*, Volume I (Ginn & Co., 1905), pages 175–76.

Examples of discontinuous functions are given in *Osgood*, pages 7–13, and the same author gives careful proofs on pages 16–18 and 41–43 of properties of continuous functions which we have stated. The reader will also find proofs in *Burkhardt-Rasor*, pages 132–35, and *Wilson*, pages 42–43.

Proofs of the existence of the definite integral are given in *Osgood*, pages 18–19, *Burkhardt-Rasor*, pages 151–53, and *Wilson*, pages 50–54. Improper integrals are discussed in *Wilson*, pages 352–78, and double integrals are considered on pages 315–24. Curve integrals have an especially thorough treatment in *Osgood's* Chapter IV. Somewhat briefer are *Wilson's* treatment in pages 288–303 and *Pierpont's* in pages 150–62. *Burkhardt-Rasor* gives pages 156–62 to this subject, and *Townsend* pages 47–59.

Implicit functions are discussed, and the existence theorems are accurately stated and proved in detail, in *Osgood*, pages 59–70. See also *Wilson*, pages 117–25.

CHAPTER IV

COMPLEX FUNCTIONS THAT HAVE DERIVATIVES

20. **Functions and limits.** With the complex variable we repeat almost word for word the definition of a function which was used for real variables: *The dependent variable w is a function of the independent variable z if to each value of the latter corresponds one or more values of the former.* It is implied here that w is a complex variable, as well as z, and we should recall that a real variable is a special case of a complex variable. A function may be defined for all values of z, but more frequently the region of definition will be taken as a connected region T, which may or may not be closed, such as we have used in Chapter III.

A polynomial in z is clearly a function of z, as is also the quotient of two polynomials, a *rational function*. The former is defined for all values of z, but the region of definition of the latter cannot include the points where the denominator vanishes; these points are considered as boundary points of the region of definition.

It is clear in the case of a simple function like z^2 that it can be expressed in the form $u(x, y) + iv(x, y)$, where u and v are real functions of x and y; thus

$$z^2 = (x + iy)^2 = (x^2 - y^2) + i(2xy) .$$

A moment's reflection shows us that even in the most general case where w is a function of z, we must, since w

is complex, have $w = u + iv$, and u and v must be determined for each value of x and y; i.e., they must be functions of x and y. Conversely, every expression $u(x, y) + iv(x, y)$ represents a function of $z = x + iy$, for to determine z is to determine x and y, and through them the functions u and v. Thus $x - iy$ is a function of $z = x + iy$, though it is not a polynomial or rational function in terms of z, and we shall see later that it does not belong to the class which we designate *analytic functions* of z.

A sequence of complex numbers is geometrically represented by a sequence of points, such as was discussed in Chapter III. There are, then, two equivalent definitions for the limit of a sequence. According to the one, the infinite sequence $z_1, z_2, \ldots$, where $z_1 = x_1 + iy_1$, $z_2 = x_2 + iy_2, \ldots$, approaches $Z = X + iY$ as a limit if and only if $x_1, x_2, \ldots$, approaches X as a limit, and $y_1, y_2, \ldots$, approaches Y as a limit. The other definition would make each circle about Z contain *all* the terms of the sequence after a certain mth, m being assignable for each circle. This is equivalent to requiring that to each positive real number ϵ there correspond an m such that $|z_n - Z| < \epsilon$ for all $n > m$.

Following again the definitions for real functions, we say that $w = f(z)$ has the limit W as z approaches Z if for each z-sequence approaching Z the corresponding w-sequence approaches W. The ϵ, δ definition requires that for each positive real number ϵ a positive real δ exist such that $|W - w| < \epsilon$ for every z verifying the inequality $|Z - z| < \delta$. The question arises how this is to be represented geometrically. If we write $w = u + iv$, $z = x + iy$, it is clear that we are concerned here with four real variables, u, v, x, y, and a figure in four dimensions is suggested. It is usual, however, to think of the values of w as represented by points of a w-plane, whose co-ordinates are u and v, and of the function $w=f(z)$ as setting up a correspondence between the points of the z- and w-planes. Thus the foregoing ϵ, δ definition requires that to each circle in the w-plane with W as center and ϵ as radius there correspond a circle in the z-plane with Z as center and radius δ such that w is in the former circle whenever z is in the latter.

A necessary and sufficient condition that w have the limit $U+iV$ as z approaches Z is given by the simultaneous relations

$$\lim_{x=X,\,y=Y} u=U\ ,\quad \lim_{x=X,\,y=Y} v=V\ .$$

If $f(z)$ is defined throughout a neighborhood of Z, it is continuous at Z if the limit of $f(z)$ as Z approaches z is $f(z)$; it is continuous throughout a region if continuous at each point of the region. If $f(z)=u(x,y)+iv(x,y)$, the continuity of $f(z)$ is equivalent to that of $u(x,y)$ and $v(x,y)$. We could thus deduce properties of continuous functions of a complex variable analogous to those indicated in the preceding chapter for real variables (see p. 23).

21. **Necessary conditions for the existence of a derivative.** To define the derivative of a function of a complex variable $f(z)$ we use the same formula as for real variables:

$$f'(z)=\frac{d}{dz}f(z)=\lim_{\Delta z=0}\frac{f(z+\Delta z)-f(z)}{\Delta z}=\lim_{\Delta z=0}\frac{\Delta f}{\Delta z}\ .$$

On account of the formal similarity of fundamental operations with complex and with real numbers, a polynomial

$$a_0 z^n + a_1 z^{n-1} + \cdots \cdot + a_{n-1} z + a_n$$

will have the derivative

$$n a_0 z^{n-1} + (n-1) a_1 z^{n-2} + \cdots \cdot + a_{n-1} \, ,$$

whether the variable z and the coefficients are real or complex, and we may also carry over to the complex field the formula for the derivative of a rational function. In fact, when the functions concerned have been suitably defined, all the formulas for differentiation, as given in elementary calculus, hold when functions and variables are complex. The concluding sections of this chapter will give examples of functions thus defined.

A function which is single-valued throughout a region is *analytic throughout that region* if it has a derivative at every point of the region. The terms "monogenic," "holomorphic," and "regular" have also been used with this meaning. To call a function analytic implies that there is some region throughout which it is analytic.

The parallelism between formulas for differentiating in the real and in the complex fields should not conceal an essential difference in the two cases as regards the sort of limit involved. Since z stands for $x+iy$, the increment of z has for its real part an increment of x, and for its imaginary part i times an increment of y. Thus $\Delta z = \Delta x + i \Delta y$, and to make Δz approach zero both Δx and Δy must approach zero. We are concerned with a *double* or *two-dimensional* limit in the complex case. The existence of the derivative of a function at a point requires that the difference quotient have the same limit no matter how Δx and Δy approach zero. So simple a function as $f(z) = x - iy$ does not have a derivative at any point, for the difference quotient

$$\frac{[(x+\Delta x)-i(y+\Delta y)]-[x-iy]}{\Delta x+i\Delta y} = \frac{\Delta x-i\Delta y}{\Delta x+i\Delta y}$$

has no limit independent of the way in which Δx and Δy approach zero. For example, if we first make Δy zero and then let Δx approach zero, the limit of the difference quotient is $+1$, but if Δx first vanishes and Δy then approaches zero, the limit is -1. The condition that a function be analytic is more restrictive than appears at first glance.

The two ways in which we allowed Δz to approach zero in the foregoing example can be used to obtain equations which must hold if $f(z)$ is to be analytic. In the one case Δz becomes equal to Δx, and the latter quantity approaches zero. These steps correspond to making the difference quotient $\Delta f/\Delta z$ take the form $\Delta_x f/\Delta x$, and then passing to the limit $\partial f/\partial x$. If $f(z) = u(x, y) + iv(x, y)$ this means that the derivative must be given by the formula

$$\frac{df}{dz} = \frac{\partial f}{\partial x} = \frac{\partial u}{\partial x} + i\frac{\partial v}{\partial x}.$$

On the other hand, if Δx first vanishes, Δz has the value $i\Delta y$, and when this approaches zero, we have

$$\frac{df}{dz} = \frac{1}{i}\frac{\partial f}{\partial y} = \frac{1}{i}\left[\frac{\partial u}{\partial y}+i\frac{\partial v}{\partial y}\right] = \frac{\partial v}{\partial y} - i\frac{\partial u}{\partial y}.$$

In order that $f(z)$ be analytic, then, its partial derivatives with respect to x and y must verify the equation

$$\frac{\partial f}{\partial x} = \frac{1}{i} \frac{\partial f}{\partial y} .$$

If we use the equivalent expressions given above in terms of partial derivatives of u and v, the real parts must be equal, and similarly for the imaginary parts. The resulting equations

$$(1) \qquad \frac{\partial u}{\partial x} = \frac{\partial v}{\partial y} , \qquad \frac{\partial u}{\partial y} = -\frac{\partial v}{\partial x} ,$$

whose verification at a point $z_0 = x_0 + iy_0$ is a necessary condition that $f(z) = u + iv$ have a derivative at z_0, are called the *Cauchy-Riemann equations*, from the two mathematicians who showed their importance in the theory of functions of a complex variable.

22. **Sufficient conditions.** Since the Cauchy-Riemann equations (1) express merely the fact that the limit of $\Delta f / \Delta z$ is the same for two particular ways in which Δz may approach zero, it is not at all self-evident that they express a *sufficient* condition that $f(z)$ be analytic. However, we shall prove that this is the case provided we add the hypothesis that the first partial derivatives of u and v exist throughout a neighborhood of z_0 and are continuous at z_0. We can then write (see formula (4), p. 28)

$$\Delta u = \frac{\partial u}{\partial x} \Delta x + \frac{\partial u}{\partial y} \Delta y + \epsilon_1 \Delta x + \epsilon_2 \Delta y ,$$

$$\Delta v = \frac{\partial v}{\partial x} \Delta x + \frac{\partial u}{\partial x} \Delta y + \epsilon_3 \Delta x + \epsilon_4 \Delta y$$

where ϵ_1 and ϵ_2 approach zero when Δx and Δy approach zero, and similarly for Δv. But the Cauchy-Riemann equations enable us to replace $\partial u/\partial y$ by $-\partial v/\partial x$, and $\partial v/\partial y$ by $\partial u/\partial x$, so that we have

$$\Delta u+i\Delta v=\frac{\partial u}{\partial x}\Delta x-\frac{\partial v}{\partial x}\Delta y+\epsilon_1\Delta x+\epsilon_2\Delta y$$

$$+i\left(\frac{\partial v}{\partial x}\Delta x+\frac{\partial u}{\partial x}\Delta y+\epsilon_3\Delta x+\epsilon_4\Delta y\right) \quad + adding$$

$$=\left(\frac{\partial u}{\partial x}+i\frac{\partial v}{\partial x}\right)(\Delta x+i\Delta y)+\zeta_1\Delta x+\zeta_2\Delta y \ ,$$

where ζ_1 and ζ_2 are complex variables whose limit is zero when Δx and Δy approach zero. When we divide the foregoing expressions by $\Delta x+i\Delta y$ the result is $\partial u/\partial x+i\partial y/\partial x$ plus the sum of two expressions, each of which has the limit zero. The first of these two expressions, for example, is the product of ζ_1 and $\Delta x/(\Delta x+i\Delta y)$. The absolute value of this last function is never greater than

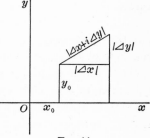

FIG. 11

1, for it is equal to $|\Delta x|/|\Delta x+i\Delta y|$, and Figure 11 shows that the numerator is the length of the base of a right triangle (unless it is zero) and the denominator is the length of the hypothenuse. But ζ_1 approaches zero, so that its product by a function of Δx and Δy whose absolute value is never greater than 1 must have the limit zero. Similarly for the other expression, so that we have

$$\lim_{\Delta z=0}\frac{\Delta f}{\Delta z}=\lim_{\Delta x=0,\ \Delta y=0}\frac{\Delta u+i\Delta v}{\Delta x+i\Delta y}=\frac{\partial u}{\partial x}+i\frac{\partial v}{\partial x} \ ,$$

and the existence of the derivative is thus established.

With these results as a guide we can readily set up analytic functions other than rational or algebraic ones. Examples are given in sections 23, 24, and 25.

The supposition made above that the first partial derivatives of u and v are continuous may seem restrictive, but it has been shown by Goursat that from the mere existence of a derivative of $f(z)$ at each point of a region T the continuity of that derivative follows, and hence the first partial derivatives of u and v *must* be continuous if $u+iv$ is analytic.

We shall show in Chapter VI that if $f(z)$ is analytic throughout a region, not only the *first* partial derivatives of u and v, but all those of higher orders also exist throughout that region. This being granted, let us differentiate the first of the Cauchy-Riemann equations (1) with respect to x, the second with respect to y, and add the resulting equations. The result is *Laplace's equation*

$$(2) \qquad \frac{\partial^2 u}{\partial x^2} + \frac{\partial^2 u}{\partial y^2} = 0 \ .$$

By differentiating the first of equations (1) with respect to y, the second with respect to x, and subtracting, we find that v also verifies Laplace's equation. Thus, if we seek to set up an analytic function, our choice of both u and v must be made among the solutions of Laplace's equation. This condition is necessary, but taken alone it is not sufficient. If, however, the function u is so chosen, v is given by a simple formula. To obtain this we note that the curve integral

$$V = \int_{(x_0,\, y_0)}^{(x,\, y)} -\frac{\partial u}{\partial y}dx + \frac{\partial u}{\partial x}dy \ ,$$

which verifies the condition for independence of path (see p. 36), has the partial derivatives

$$\frac{\partial V}{\partial x} = -\frac{\partial u}{\partial y}, \qquad \frac{\partial V}{\partial y} = \frac{\partial u}{\partial x},$$

according to the rule of page 37 for differentiating such an integral. Hence u and V satisfy equations (1), and V is a possible value for v. It can be shown that for a given u satisfying Laplace's equation, every possible v must have the form $V+C$, where C is a constant, if $u+iv$ is to be analytic.

A solution u of Laplace's equation, with continuous second partial derivatives, is called a *harmonic function*, and v, as defined above, its *harmonic conjugate*.

23. The exponential function. We have already remarked that polynomials and rational functions are analytic. We now proceed to define certain other elementary functions which are also analytic, and to state a few of their properties.

In defining the function e^z for complex values of z, where e is the natural base of logarithms ($e = 2.718 \ldots$), it is evidently desirable that when z takes the real value x, the function e^z shall be the function e^x we have already met in the calculus. Further, we should like to have it satisfy the same functional and differential equations that e^x does. Let us then see what follows if we require that e^z be so defined at every point of the z-plane that (a) it is single-valued and analytic, (b) it is the function e^x as ordinarily defined when $z = x$, (c) its derivative is e^z.

If we write

$$e^z = u + iv,$$

and if we recollect that the derivative with respect to z is equal to the partial derivative with respect to x, our requirement (c) takes the form

$$\frac{\partial}{\partial x}(u+iv)=u+iv,$$

or

$$\frac{\partial u}{\partial x}=u\ ,\qquad \frac{\partial v}{\partial x}=v\ .$$

The solution of the first of these last two equations is

$$u=e^x f(y)\ . \quad \textit{It checks}$$

Let us now substitute this value of u in the Cauchy-Riemann equation

$$\frac{\partial u}{\partial y}=-\frac{\partial v}{\partial x}\ .$$

Since $\partial v/\partial x=v$, this gives us

$$v=-\frac{\partial u}{\partial y}=-e^x\frac{d}{dy}\,f(y)\ .$$

If these values of u and v are substituted in the Cauchy-Riemann equation

$$\frac{\partial u}{\partial x}=\frac{\partial v}{\partial y}\ , \quad \textit{(1) p. 48}$$

we obtain

$$\frac{d^2}{dy^2}\,f(y)+f(y)=0\ , \quad \textit{It checks}$$

so that $f(y)$ must be of the form

$$f(y)=c_1\cos y+c_2\sin y\ ,$$

and we have

$$u = e^x f(y) = e^x (c_1 \cos y + c_2 \sin y) ,$$

$$v = -e^x \frac{d}{dy} f(y) = e^x (c_1 \sin y - c_2 \cos y) .$$

But in order that e^z may be e^x when $z = x$, i.e., when $y = 0$, we must have

$$[u]_{y=0} = e^x , \qquad [v]_{y=0} = 0 ,$$

so that

$$c_1 = 1 , \qquad c_2 = 0 ,$$

$$u = e^x \cos y , \qquad v = e^x \sin y .$$

Thus we must have

$$(3) \qquad e^z = e^{x+iy} = e^x (\cos y + i \sin y) ,$$

and this formula will therefore be taken as the definition of the exponential function e^z for complex values of z.

Let us note some consequences of the foregoing definition. In the first place, e^z verifies the functional equation

$$F(z_1 + z_2) = F(z_1) F(z_2) ,$$

for

$$e^{z_1 + z_2} = e^{x_1 + x_2}[\cos (y_1 + y_2) + i \sin (y_1 + y_2)]$$

$$= e^{x_1} e^{x_2} (\cos y_1 + i \sin y_1)(\cos y_2 + i \sin y_2)$$

$$= e^{z_1} e^{z_2} . \quad \text{by (3)}$$

If we let x vanish in (3), we have

$$(4) \qquad e^{iy} = \cos y + i \sin y ;$$

and we thus verify a special case of the foregoing functional equation,

$$e^{x+iy} = e^x e^{iy} .$$

By changing y into $-y$ we deduce from (4)

(5) $$e^{-iy} = \cos y - i \sin y .$$

The result of solving (4) and (5) for $\sin y$ and $\cos y$ is

(6) $$\cos y = \frac{e^{iy} + e^{-iy}}{2} , \ \sin y = \frac{e^{iy} - e^{-iy}}{2i} .$$

The function e^z is periodic, with period $2\pi i$. By this we mean that $e^{z+2\pi i} = e^z$. In fact,

$$e^{z+2\pi i} = e^z e^{2\pi i} = e^z (\cos 2\pi + i \sin 2\pi) = e^z .$$

Every positive or negative integral multiple of $2\pi i$ is also a period, but there are no others; for the equation

$$e^{z+a} = e^z$$

is readily reduced to $e^a = 1$. If $a = a_1 + ia_2$, we have

$$e^a = e^{a_1} (\cos a_2 + i \sin a_2) = 1,$$

so that $a_1 = 0$, $a_2 = 2n\pi$, and $a = 2n\pi i$.

24. **Trigonometric functions.** Formulas (6) hold when y is real. It is natural to use them as definitions of the functions $\cos z$ and $\sin z$ when y is replaced by the complex variable z. Thus

$$\cos z = \frac{e^{iz} + e^{-iz}}{2} = \frac{e^{ix-y} + e^{-ix+y}}{2}$$
$$= \tfrac{1}{2}[e^{-y}(\cos x + i \sin x) + e^y (\cos x - i \sin x)]$$
$$= \tfrac{1}{2}(e^y + e^{-y}) \cos x - i \tfrac{1}{2}(e^y - e^{-y}) \sin x$$
$$= \cosh y \cos x - i \sinh y \sin x ,$$

where sinh y and cosh y are the hyperbolic sine and cosine of y. Similarly

$$\sin z = \frac{e^{iz} - e^{-iz}}{2i} = \cosh y \sin x + i \sinh y \cos x .$$

The functions $\sin z$ and $\cos z$ thus defined are single-valued and continuous at every point, and their real and imaginary parts have continuous first partial derivatives which satisfy the Cauchy-Riemann equations, i.e., these functions are everywhere analytic. It follows at once from their definitions that they coincide with the real trigonometric functions $\cos x$ and $\sin x$ when $z = x$.

The reader may find it interesting to prove for himself that $\cos z$ and $\sin z$ satisfy the ordinary trigonometric identities such as

$$\sin^2 z + \cos^2 z = 1,$$

$$\sin (z_1 + z_2) = \sin z_1 \cos z_2 + \cos z_1 \sin z_2 ,$$

$$\cos \left(z + \frac{\pi}{2} \right) = -\sin z ,$$

$$\cos (z + 2n\pi) = \cos z, \quad \sin (z + 2n\pi) = \sin z .$$

The last identities express the fact that both $\sin z$ and $\cos z$ have the period $2n\pi$, where n is any positive or negative integer whatever. It would not be difficult to follow the model of our discussion of the periods of e^z and show that the periods $2n\pi$ are the only possible ones for $\cos z$ and $\sin z$.

We define the other trigonometric functions in terms of $\cos z$ and $\sin z$ by means of the familiar formulas of elementary trigonometry.

25. **The logarithmic function.** We define the logarithm as the inverse of the exponential function, i.e., the two equations

(7) $$e^w = z , \qquad w = \log z ,$$

define w as the same function of z. If w is expressed in rectangular co-ordinates (u , v) we have

$$e^u(\cos v + i \sin v) = z ,$$

so that e^u is the absolute value of z, and v is an amplitude of z. If we designate these by r and θ, respectively, it follows that u is the logarithm of the positive real number r according to the usual definition of a real logarithm to base e, while v is θ. The result is expressed by the formula

(8) $$w = \log z = \log r + i \theta .$$

The logarithmic function is infinitely many-valued, for if θ_1 is the value of θ such that $0 \leqq \theta_1 < 2\pi$, the same point z has also the amplitude $\theta = \theta_1 + 2n\pi$, where n is any integer whatever, positive or negative, and we have

(9) $$w = \log z = \log r + i(\theta_1 + 2n\pi) .$$

There is but one value of z which has no logarithm, the value $z = 0$.

When we give n a particular value in (9) we have a *branch* of the logarithmic function which is single-valued and continuous throughout the interior of every region in which lie neither the origin nor points of the positive x-axis. To prove that such a branch is analytic throughout every region of the sort just indicated it is convenient here to use the formula

$$\frac{dz}{dw} = \frac{1}{\dfrac{dw}{dz}} ,$$

which we shall establish in Chapter V (see p. 63). From the first of equations (7) we have

$$\frac{dz}{dw} = \frac{d}{dw} e^w = e^w = z ,$$

so that the preceding formula gives

$$\frac{dw}{dz} = \frac{1}{z} ,$$

and $w = \log z$ has thus a derivative at every point at which we have defined a branch of this function.

The function $\log z$ can be shown to satisfy the general formulas for real logarithms. In particular, we have the two relations

(10)
$$\log (z_1 z_2) = \log z_1 + \log z_2 ,$$
$$\log z^a = a \log z .$$

In the former relation we may give to $\log z_1$ and $\log z_2$ any of the infinitely many values corresponding to formula (9); for each choice of such values there is a value of $\log (z_1 z_2)$ which verifies the above formula. The latter relation, easily proved to hold for suitably chosen branches of the logarithmic functions involved when a is a rational real number, suggests that we define z^a for all values of a, real or complex, by means of the formula

$$z^a = e^{a \log z} .$$

We have seen that log z is an infinitely many-valued function, and the same will be true for z^a unless a is a rational real number. The second of relations (10) is true for each value of log z and the corresponding value of z^a, provided the value of log z^a is suitably chosen.

Similarly we define a^z by the formula

$$a^z = e^{z \log a} .$$

Here the infinitely many values of log a give rise to infinitely many functions which satisfy the foregoing definition, and in any particular case we should agree as to which one we mean.

The function $w = \sin^{-1} z$ is defined as the solution of the equation

$$z = \sin w = \frac{e^{iw} - e^{-iw}}{2i} .$$

The exponential form on the right allows us to reduce the equation to a quadratic in e^{iw}, whose solution gives

$$e^{iw} = iz \pm \sqrt{1 - z^2} .$$

From this result we may express the inverse sine of z as a logarithm, and similarly for the other inverse trigonometric functions.

26. **References.** The material of sections 20, 21, and 22 is covered by *Osgood* in pages 214–32. *Townsend* is especially full here, Chapter II being devoted to definitions of functions and limits and properties of continuous functions, while derivatives, the Cauchy-Riemann equations, and Laplace's equation are treated in pages 43–46, 82–89, 92–95. *Burkhardt-Rasor* is briefer in pages 167–81, and the same is true of *Goursat-Hedrick*, pages 3–13, *Pierpont*, pages 163–86, and *Wilson*, pages 157–59 and 476–77.

The elementary functions which we have considered in the last three sections of the present chapter are discussed similarly in *Osgood*, pages 248–58, and *Townsend*, pages 122–55. *Wilson* devotes to these topics only pages 159–62. *Burkhardt-Rasor* in pages 216–24 and 294–304, *Goursat-Hedrick* in pages 23–32, and *Pierpont* in pages 102–28 proceed from definitions in terms of infinite series, except that the first-mentioned book defines the logarithm by means of a definite integral.

On page 50 we have referred to Goursat's theorem that if the derivative of a function exists at every point of a region it must be continuous. This is a corollary of his proof of Cauchy's integral theorem, references to which will be found at the end of Chapter VI.

CHAPTER V

APPLICATIONS IN GEOMETRY AND PHYSICS

27. Conformal mapping. It is not our object in this chapter to give a general survey of the geometrical and physical applications of the theory of functions of a complex variable, but only to consider certain especially interesting cases. On the geometrical side we shall confine ourselves to the study of equations $w = f(z)$ regarded as transformations which bring about a correspondence between points of the w- and z-planes.

In a map of a piece of the earth's surface small enough to be thought of as plane, a straight line on the earth will in general be represented by a curved line on the map, and points an inch apart in one part of the map may represent points a mile apart on the earth, while in another part of the map the scale may be two miles to the inch. We are familiar with such conditions in Mercator's charts. But it is a desideratum that each point on the map correspond to one point of the region mapped, and vice versa. That is, if we set up a uv-co-ordinate system in the map, and an xy-system in the region mapped, then u and v should be defined and single-valued throughout the xy-region, and their corresponding values should cover once, without duplication, the uv-region. If we use complex variables $w = u + iv$ and $z = x + iy$, and the region S of the z-plane is mapped on the region Σ of the w-plane, then w is a function of z since a value of w corresponds to each value of z. If we write

$w = f(z)$ it is necessary for point-to-point correspondence that the *mapping function* $f(z)$ be defined throughout S and give but one w in Σ for each z in S and that the *inverse* function $z = F(w)$ be defined throughout Σ and give but one z in S for each w in Σ.

A second requirement that at once suggests itself is that both $f(z)$ and $F(w)$ be continuous. And finally, though the scale of the map may be different at different points, it should be constant at each point in the manner

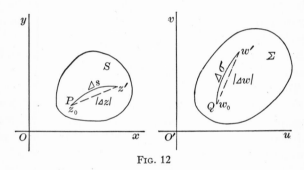

Fɪɢ. 12

indicated in the following paragraph, in which case the map is said to be *conformal*.

Let us examine a little more closely this last property of conformal mapping. Starting from a point P of S corresponding to the complex number z_0, we draw a curve segment of length Δs. In Σ there corresponds the point Q belonging to the number w_0, and a curve segment of length $\Delta\sigma$. If we let Δs approach zero, $\Delta\sigma$ will also approach zero. The *scale* is said to be constant at Q if the limit of $\Delta\sigma/\Delta s$ is the same for *all* curve segments whose initial point is P. Now if z_0 is the initial point of a curve segment of length Δs, and z' is the terminal point, the length of the chord subtending the curve segment is $|z'-z_0| = |\Delta z|$; similarly $|\Delta w|$ is the length of the chord subtending the corresponding curve segment in Σ. Since the limit of the ratio of curve lengths is the same as that of chord lengths, we have

$$\lim \frac{\Delta \sigma}{\Delta s} = \lim \left| \frac{\Delta w}{\Delta z} \right|.$$

The foregoing relation shows that our third requirement is satisfied, in case the other two are, if $f(z)$ is analytic throughout S, for in that case the limit of $\Delta w/\Delta z$ is $f'(z_0)$, no matter how Δz approaches zero. The scale function at z_0 is $|f'(z_0)|$.

To what extent are the first and second requirements satisfied, given that $f(z)$ is a function analytic throughout a neighborhood of a point z_0? We have before us a problem regarding implicit functions. Solving the equation $w=f(z)$ for z as a function of w is equivalent, if $f(z) = f_1(x, y)+if_2(x, y)$, to solving for x and y the pair of equations

$$u=f_1(x, y), \qquad v=f_2(x, y)$$

On page 40 we saw that if the Jacobian determinant

$$\begin{vmatrix} \dfrac{\partial f_1}{\partial x} & \dfrac{\partial f_1}{\partial y} \\[2ex] \dfrac{\partial f_2}{\partial x} & \dfrac{\partial f_2}{\partial y} \end{vmatrix}$$

does not vanish at (x_0, y_0), the partial derivatives concerned being continuous, then there exist unique solutions $x=F_1(u, v)$, $y=F_2(u, v)$, satisfied by u_0, v_0, x_0, y_0, and such that F_1 and F_2 are single-valued and continuous throughout a neighborhood of (u_0, v_0). Since $f(z)$ is analytic throughout a neighborhood of z_0, the Cauchy-Riemann equations hold at that point and the Jacobian determinant above reduces to

$$\left[\left(\frac{\partial f_1}{\partial x} \right)^2 + \left(\frac{\partial f_2}{\partial x} \right)^2 \right]_{z=z_0} = \left| \frac{\partial f(z)}{\partial x} \right|^2_{z=z_0} = |f'(z_0)|^2 .$$

Hence the Jacobian determinant vanishes at (x_0, y_0) when and only when $f'(z_0) = 0$. Further, under our hypotheses the partial derivatives of f_1 and f_2 are continuous throughout a neighborhood of (x_0, y_0). Thus if $f'(z_0)$ *is not zero*, we can apply our theorem regarding implicit functions, and we conclude that *there is a neighborhood S of z_0 and a neighborhood Σ of w_0 which are mapped on each other one-to-one and conformally by the transformation $w = f(z)$*. We here do not say how large either S or Σ is; in many cases S must be only part of the total region throughout which $f(z)$ is single-valued and analytic.

Let us note that the inverse function $z = F(w)$ is analytic throughout a neighborhood of w_0, and its derivative at that point is given by the well-known formula

$$\frac{dz}{dw} = \frac{1}{\dfrac{dw}{dz}} .$$

In fact, the corresponding equation in which Δ's replace d's is true because to each Δw sufficiently small corresponds one and only one small Δz, and Δz is not zero unless Δw is zero. By letting Δw approach zero we obtain the foregoing equation connecting derivatives.

28. **Preservation of angles.** The transformation $w = f(z)$ which we have been discussing gives a map which

is *isogonal* as well as conformal. By this we mean that the angle between two curve segments having their initial points at z_0 is always equal to the angle between the corresponding two curve segments at w_0. To show that

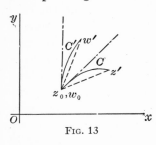

FIG. 13

this is so, regard the w-plane as superposed on the z-plane so that w_0 coincides with z_0 and the u- and v-axes have the same directions as the x- and y-axes, respectively. On a curve segment C with initial point at z_0 take a point z'. To this corresponds a curve segment C' with initial point at w_0, and a point w' on C' as shown in Figure 13. We write

$$\frac{\Delta w}{\Delta z} = \frac{w' - w_0}{z' - z_0} .$$

Now the amplitude of a quotient is obtained by subtracting the amplitude of the denominator from that of the numerator, i.e., it is the angle measured from the vector representing the denominator to that representing the numerator. Hence the amplitude of $\Delta w / \Delta z$ is the angle from the chord of C which begins at z_0 and ends at z' to the corresponding chord of C'. When we let Δz approach zero the directions of chords become the directions of tangents, so that the amplitude of dw/dz is the angle from the tangent of C at z_0 to the tangent of C' at the coincident point w_0. This angle is therefore constant for all curve segments with initial point at z_0. It follows at once that the angle from the tangent of such a curve segment C_1 to that of another curve segment C_2 is equal to the corresponding angle for corresponding curve segments C_1' and C_2'.

Our transformation is, in fact, *isogonal with preservation of angles*. This term is used in contrast to the term *isogonal with reversal of angles*, which applies to the case where the angle from C_1 to C_2 is always the negative of the angle from C_1' to C_2'. It can be shown that if we limit ourselves to transformations in which the functions have continuous first partial derivatives with non-vanishing Jacobian in S, a conformal transformation must be isogonal in one of these two senses. If it is isogonal with preservation of angles, the Cauchy-Riemann equations must be satisfied, and the transformation can be put in the form $w = f(z)$, where $f(z)$ is analytic throughout S. If the transformation is isogonal with reversal of angles, the corresponding equation is $\bar{w} = f(z)$, where $\bar{w}$ denotes the conjugate of w; i.e., $\bar{w} = u - iv$ if $w = u + iv$.

So interesting a connection between subjects apparently so far apart as conformal maps and the theory of functions of a complex variable deserves more detailed study. We shall accordingly examine the maps corresponding to some of the simpler transformations $w = f(z)$. In some cases we can consider them as the result of mere displacements of the original configurations. If the relation is not so simple, let us recall the first comparison we would be apt to make between a Mercator's chart and any other flat map of the same part of the earth's surface, which would thus be a map of the Mercator's map. We would probably first note that certain lines or curves in the second map correspond to parallels of latitude and meridians of longitude in the other. The knowledge of these curves enables us to determine the point-to-point correspondence between the maps. So in general the mapping is in a sense described when we determine what curves in the uv-plane correspond to parallels to the x- and y-axes.

29. Linear transformations. The *general linear transformation* is that given by

$$(1) \qquad w = \frac{az+b}{cz+d},$$

where, in order to avoid cases in which the right side of the equation either has no value or reduces to a constant, we suppose that $ad - bc \neq 0$. On this assumption we see both c and d cannot be zero simultaneously. If $c = 0$, we have

$$w = \frac{a}{d}z + \frac{b}{d},$$

and our transformation reduces to an *integral linear transformation*, in which the coefficient of z is not zero, since a and c cannot both vanish. If c does not vanish, we write

$$w = \frac{az+b}{cz+d} = \frac{a}{c} + \frac{bc-ad}{c} \cdot \frac{1}{cz+d}.$$

The successive auxiliary transformations

$$z' = cz + d,$$
$$z'' = \frac{1}{z'},$$
$$w = \frac{a}{c} + \frac{bc-ad}{c} z'',$$

change each z into the same w as would the general linear transformation (1). It remains, then, to study integral linear transformations and the second of the auxiliary transformations.

The integral linear transformation

(2) $$w = Az + B,$$

where $A \neq 0$, is equivalent to a combination of the two special types

$$Z = Az ,$$

$$w = Z + B .$$

The latter transformation is easily recognized as a *translation*. We have the map of the Z-plane on the w-plane if we superpose the former on the latter so that the axes in the one coincide with the respective axes in the other, and then move the whole XY-plane, but not the uv-axes, in the direction and to the distance which are the direction and absolute value of the vector corresponding to the complex number B. As to the transformation, $Z = Az$, we know that multiplying z by a complex number A multiplies the absolute value of z by $|A|$, and adds the amplitude of A to that of z. That is, if we let the axes of the Z-plane coincide with those of the z-plane, and then remain fixed, we shall obtain the map of the z-plane on the Z-plane by rotating the former about the origin through the angle which is the amplitude of A, and magnifying distances measured from the origin by the factor $|A|$. Thus the transformation (2) is equivalent to a rotation, a stretching from the origin, and a translation of the whole plane, following each other as indicated. It is one definition of similar figures that they are carried into each other by such a transformation. In particular, straight lines go into straight lines and circles into circles. Since angles are preserved, parallels to the x- and y-axes become two sets of parallel lines in the uv-plane which cut each other at right angles.

The transformation $w = 1/z$, in which we have merely renamed the variable z' and z'' in the second of our auxiliary transformations, can be regarded, when the axes of the w- and z-planes are placed in coincidence, as carrying a point z into a point $1/z$. We know that the absolute value of the latter is the reciprocal of the absolute value of z, and its amplitude is the negative of the amplitude of z. A transformation which changes a point into one whose absolute value is the reciprocal of that belonging to the point, but leaves the amplitude unchanged, is called a *transformation by reciprocal radii*; it is isogonal with reversal of angles. A transformation which changes a point into one whose amplitude is the negative of that of the first while the absolute value is unchanged is a *reflection on the axis of reals*; it is also isogonal with reversal of angles. The transformation $w = 1/z$ is equivalent to these two transformations in succession, and is isogonal with preservation of angles. Let us note that the transformation is one-to-one between the whole z-plane and the whole w-plane with these exceptions; to $z = 0$ corresponds no w point and to $w = 0$ corresponds no z point. To avoid this difficulty we introduce the *ideal* points $w = \infty$ and $z = \infty$, defined as corresponding to $z = 0$ and $w = 0$, respectively. All the finite z points plus the ideal point $z = \infty$ constitute the *enlarged* z-plane, and similarly for the *enlarged* w-plane. The correspondence is one-to-one between the two enlarged planes.

We shall now prove that this transformation also carries circles into circles provided straight lines are included as limiting cases of circles. Written in Cartesian co-ordinates, $w = 1/z$ becomes

$$u = \frac{x}{x^2+y^2}, \qquad v = \frac{-y}{x^2+y^2},$$

or

$$x = \frac{u}{u^2+v^2}, \qquad y = \frac{-v}{u^2+v^2}.$$

The equation

$$(3) \qquad a(x^2+y^2)+bx+cy+d = 0,$$

where a, b, c, d, are real, becomes

$$(4) \qquad d(u^2+v^2)+bu-cv+a = 0$$

when we make the substitutions indicated above. Every circle which does not pass through the origin has an equation of type (3) in which a and d are both not zero, but in this case (4) also represents a circle not passing through the origin. Every circle through the origin is represented by (3) if $d = 0$, $a \neq 0$, and either b or c does not vanish; but (4) is then the equation of a straight line not passing through the origin. Similarly, a straight line not passing through the origin goes into a circle through the origin, and a straight line through the origin goes into a straight line through the origin. Thus every member of the family of straight lines and circles goes into a member of that family. A transformation with this property is often called a *circular transformation*.

Since the integral linear transformation (2) is also a circular transformation, and since the general linear transformation (1) is equivalent to a succession of circular transformations, (1) is also circular. We can easily see how (1) transforms parallels to the x- and y-axes by considering the effect of the auxiliary transformations. Obviously the integral linear transformation (2) changes such parallels into mutually orthogonal systems of parallel lines, while under the transformation $w = 1/z$ these systems become two systems of circles, mutually orthogonal, all those of each set having a common tangent and a common point of tangency. The latter points for the two systems coincide. An integral linear transformation carries this configuration into another of the same kind.

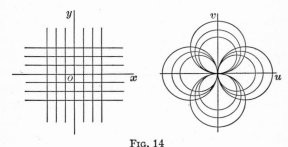

Fig. 14

Since the general linear transformation (1) is equivalent to a succession of transformations of the types just considered, it evidently changes parallels to the axes in the z-plane into systems of circles of the sort just described in the w-plane. Figure 14 illustrates the map for $w = 1/z$. The circles shown correspond to the equations (4) which come from giving equations (3) the forms $x = $ constant and $y = $ constant. Similarly, curves $u = $ constant, or $v = $ constant correspond to such systems of circles in the xy-plane.

30. **Transformations corresponding to power functions.** The function z^m, where m is a positive integer greater than 1, is analytic at every point, and its deriva-

tive vanishes only for $z=0$. Hence this transformation maps conformally a neighborhood of every z-point except the origin upon a neighborhood of some w-point. At the origin the mapping is not conformal; in fact, no neighborhood of the z-origin is mapped in a one-to-one way on a w-region, as we now proceed to show.

In Chapter II, we saw that if we use polar co-ordinates, so that z is $r(\cos \theta + i \sin \theta)$, we have

$$w = r^m(\cos m\theta + i \sin m\theta) .$$

Thus, if the w- and z-planes are placed so that origins and initial axes correspond, we get a w-point from a z-point by changing the absolute value from r to r^m, and multiplying the amplitude by m. If we think of a half-ray with initial point at $z=0$ as sweeping out the z-plane by one complete revolution about its initial point, the corresponding w-ray sweeps out the w-plane m times. To each w-point correspond m points of the z-plane, and this is true no matter how small a circle about $z=0$ we are considering. Instead of the relation being isogonal at $z=0$, angles between lines meeting there correspond to angles m times as large in the w-plane.

Lines parallel to the x- and y-axes go into algebraic curves which we shall not here investigate. The situation is simpler for the mutually orthogonal systems $r=$ constant and $\theta=$ constant, which represent circles about the origin and lines through the origin. These go into curves of the same types in the w-plane but with different radii and amplitudes.

31. **Transformations corresponding to other elementary functions.** We shall here consider maps given by the functions discussed in Chapter IV, sections 23–25.

By the transformation $w = e^z$ there corresponds one and only one w to each z. Since the derivative of e^z is this function itself, which vanishes for no value of z, a neighborhood of each z-point is mapped one-to-one and conformally on a neighborhood of the corresponding w-point. This mapping is not, however, one-to-one for the whole z- and w-planes, for if w_0 corresponds to z_0 it also corresponds to all points $z_0 + 2n\pi i$. Let us then divide the z-plane into strips by the lines

$$y = 2n\pi , \qquad n = 0, 1, -1, 2, -2, \ldots ,$$

and let each strip include its lower but not its upper boundary. Each strip, thus defined, is mapped in a one-to-one way upon the whole w-plane with the exception of the point $w = 0$ to which no z-point corresponds.

The equations

$$u = e^x \cos y , \qquad v = e^x \sin y ,$$

show that the point whose rectangular co-ordinates are (u , v) has the polar co-ordinates

$$R = e^x , \qquad \Theta = y .$$

Hence the segments of lines $x = $ constant that are cut off by boundaries of strips become circles about the origin in the w-plane, and lines $y = $ constant become half-rays with initial point at the w-origin.

On account of the identity $\sin z = -\cos (z + \pi/2)$ it will be sufficient in studying transformations corresponding to the sine and cosine functions to consider only the map corresponding to $\cos z$. This function is single-valued and analytic at every z-point. Its derivative, $-\sin z$, has been expressed in terms of x and y on a previous page; it vanishes only when both the equations

$$\cosh y \sin x = 0 , \qquad \sinh y \cos x = 0 ,$$

are satisfied. Since $\cosh y$ cannot vanish, we must have, from the first of these equations, $\sin x = 0$, and since $\cos x$ is then ± 1, the second equation gives $\sinh y = 0$. The only solutions are

$$x = n\pi , \; y = 0 , \; n = 0, \; \pm 1, \; \pm 2, \; \ldots \ldots ,$$

and this means that the only points where $\sin z = 0$ are the points $z = n\pi$. For all other points, a neighborhood of a z-point is mapped one-to-one and conformally on a neighborhood of the corresponding w-point by the transformation $w = \cos z$. The question of the correspondence of the two planes as wholes we will not examine in detail, but such an examination would show that if the z-plane were divided into strips by the lines $x = n\pi \, (n = 0, \; \pm 1, \; \pm 2, \; \ldots \ldots)$, each strip, including a suitably chosen part of its boundaries, would be in one-to-one correspondence with the whole w-plane. It can also be shown that lines $x = $ constant and $y = $ constant correspond to systems of hyperbolas and ellipses in the w-plane, these systems including limiting cases.

The transformation $w = \log z$ is equivalent to $e^w = z$, hence its discussion would merely repeat, with the letters w and z interchanged, what we have said about the transformation $w = e^z$. It is here the w-plane which is to be divided into strips by the lines $v = 2n\pi$, and the whole z-plane with the exception of the point $z = 0$ is then mapped in a one-to-one way upon each strip exclusive of one boundary. A circle about the z-origin corresponds to segments of a line $u = $ constant, one segment lying in each of the strips just described, and a half-ray with initial point at $z = 0$ corresponds to a line $v = $ constant in each strip. The equations

$$e^u \cos v = x , \qquad e^u \sin v = y ,$$

readily yield the equations of the curves in the w-plane that correspond to parallels to the x- and y-axes.

32. **Two-dimensional fluid motion.** Let us suppose a fluid to move between two parallel planes, which will be considered horizontal, in such a way that a vertical line of particles moves so as to remain a vertical line and each particle is always at a constant depth. We can then discuss the motion of the fluid as though it took place in a horizontal plane, the fluid being thought of, if we wish, as *concentrated on that plane* with a certain surface density. At each point of this plane, in which we place xy-axes, the fluid will at a given time have a velocity v, with components v_x and v_y. As a first restriction on our general problem we will take up only the case in which v_x and v_y depend on x and y, but are the same for all time at each point, i.e., they are not functions of t. Further, we will suppose the surface density a constant with respect to x, y, and t. Such a flow is called a *steady movement of an incompressible fluid*. We assume v_x and v_y as continuous, with continuous first partial derivatives. Under these assumptions the total amount of fluid entering a fixed region of the plane in a given time must be equal to the amount leaving that region; or, if a quantity of fluid leaving is considered a negative quantity entering, the algebraic sum of quantities entering must be zero.

Let us now consider the total quantity of fluid entering, in unit time, a rectangle whose sides are parallel to the co-ordinate axes. If the velocity v were constant in magnitude and in direction as shown in Figure 15, the amount flowing in unit time to the right across the segment AD of a parallel to Oy would be equal to the surface density ρ multiplied by the area of the parallelogram $ABCD$, whose side DC gives the numerical value and the direction of the velocity. The rectangle $AB'C'D$

Fig. 15

has obviously the same area as the parallelogram, so that the latter area is the product of the component velocity v_x by AD. If v_x were negative we would use the same product multiplied by ρ to measure the quantity (now negative) flowing to the right. In either case we can express a flow to the right as a flow to the left by changing the sign of its measure. If v varies with x and y, let us, to be more specific, designate A as the point x_0, y_0, and D as x_0, Y_0. Divide AD into n segments each of length Δy. Across each of these the velocity differs little from that at its lowest point, so that the total quantity flowing in unit time to the right across AD is given approximately by the sum

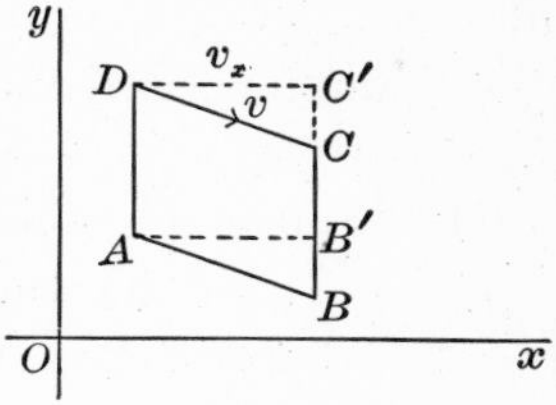

$$\rho[v_x(x_0, y_0)\Delta y + v_x(x_0, y_1)\Delta y + \ \ldots \ + v_x(x_0, y_{n-1})\Delta y]$$

and is given exactly by the limit of this sum, which has the value

$$\rho \int_{y_0}^{Y_0} v_x(x_0, y)dy \ .$$

The negative of this expression measures the flow when regarded as a flow to the left. Similarly

$$\rho \int_{x_0}^{X_0} v_y(x,\, y_0)dx$$

measures the flow upward across a segment of the line $y = y_0$, and its negative the flow when regarded as a downward one.

If we take a rectangle whose sides are on the lines

$$x = x_0\, , \qquad x = X_0\, , \qquad y = y_0\, , \qquad y = Y_0\, ,$$

the total flow into the rectangle is the sum of the flow to the right across the left-hand vertical boundary, the flow to the left across the right-hand boundary, the flow upward across the lower boundary, and the flow downward across the upper boundary. In unit time, the sum of these quantities divided by ρ is

$$\int_{y_0}^{Y_0} v_x(x_0,\, y)dy - \int_{y_0}^{Y_0} v_x(X_0,\, y)dy + \int_{x_0}^{X_0} v_y(x,\, y_0)dx$$
$$- \int_{x_0}^{X_0} v_y(x,\, Y_0)dx\, .$$

But since, for example,

$$\int_{x_0}^{X_0} \frac{\partial v_x}{\partial x}\, dx = v_x(X_0,\, y) - v_x(x_0,\, y)\, ,$$

the foregoing sum can be written

$$-\int_{y_0}^{Y_0}\int_{x_0}^{X_0} \frac{\partial v_x}{\partial x}\, dx\, dy - \int_{x_0}^{X_0}\int_{y_0}^{Y_0} \frac{\partial v_y}{\partial y}\, dy\, dx$$
$$= -\int_{x_1}^{X_0}\int_{y_0}^{Y_0} \left[\frac{\partial v_x}{\partial x} + \frac{\partial v_y}{\partial y}\right] dx\, dy\, .$$

The value of this expression, which is proportional to the total quantity of fluid entering the rectangle in unit time, must be zero for *every* rectangle in the fluid's surface whose sides are parallel to the axes. The integrand, being continuous, must vanish at every point (x , y); otherwise about a point at which it did not vanish we could take a sufficiently small rectangle with sides parallel to the axes so that within it the integrand would be everywhere of the same sign as at the point, and the integral over such a rectangle would not vanish. We thus obtain, as a necessary condition for incompressible fluid motion, the equation

(5) $$\frac{\partial v_x}{\partial x} + \frac{\partial v_y}{\partial y} = 0 ,$$

which must be satisfied at every point of the region where the flow is taking place.

An *irrotational* flow is defined as one for which there is a function U such that

$$\frac{\partial U}{\partial x} = v_x , \qquad \frac{\partial U}{\partial y} = v_y .$$

The function U is called a *velocity potential*. If these values of v_x and v_y are substituted in equation (5) we have Laplace's equation

$$\frac{\partial^2 U}{\partial x^2} + \frac{\partial^2 U}{\partial y^2} = 0 .$$

We saw on page 51 that there then exists a function V such that $w = U + iV$ is an analytic function of $z = x + iy$. Thus we have established contact between the theory of fluid motion and that of analytic functions of a complex variable. To use the terms employed on the page just referred to, if U has continuous second partial derivatives it is *harmonic*, and V is its *harmonic conjugate*.

A curve at every point of which the velocity potential U is constant is called a *line of level* and a curve $V = $ constant is a *line of flow*. The forward or backward direction on the tangent to a line of flow at each of its points is, in fact, the direction of the fluid velocity v at that point; for if α is the angle made by the line of flow with the x-axis, and β that made by the direction of the velocity v, we have

$$\tan \alpha = -\frac{\partial V}{\partial x} \div \frac{\partial V}{\partial y} = \frac{\partial U}{\partial y} \div \frac{\partial U}{\partial x} = \frac{v_y}{v_x} = \tan \beta \ .$$

Hence a line of flow is the path a particle of the fluid describes as it moves. The lines of level are curves perpendicular at each point to the lines of flow. Together, the level lines and lines of flow form a descriptive map of the motion.

Conversely, it is true that every analytic function $w = U + iV$ defines a flow with velocity potential U, in which the lines $U = $ constant and $V = $ constant are lines of level and lines of flow, respectively. We thus have a new interpretation associated with each of the functions discussed under the head of conformal mapping. For example, the function $w = 1/z$ corresponds to a flow with velocity potential

$$U = \frac{x}{x^2 + y^2} \ ,$$

and the level lines are one of the systems of circles shown in Figure 14, while the lines of flow are the other system, both taken in the xy-plane. The origin is a *singular point* both for the function and the flow.

33. Other physical applications. The flow of electricity and the flow of heat by what is called conduction can be described in terms of fluid motion. One who has grasped one end of a poker whose other end is in the fire may be convinced that something is flowing up the metal to his hand; and again everyone has seen the color of red or white heat spread in a metal body. This is not conceived to be an actual flow of particles of heat through the conducting body, but the analogy is so close that it may be described in those terms. Quantity of heat can be measured, and the flow between two points depends on their difference of temperature as well as their distance apart. If the temperature at each point of a flat metal plate is $u(x, y)$, not dependent on the time variable t, we have a *steady flow* of heat. The partial derivatives $\partial u/\partial x$, $\partial u/\partial y$, measuring change of temperature in the x- and y-directions, correspond to the velocities v_x and v_y in fluid motion, and the temperature function $u(x, y)$ corresponds to the velocity potential. We have again lines of flow and lines of level, the latter now being styled "isotherms," or lines of equal temperature. The real part of every analytic function of a complex variable can thus be a temperature function, its harmonic conjugate determining the lines of flow.

For the two-dimensional flow of electricity we have a similar descriptive scheme, electric potential here playing the rôle of temperature in the heat problem and velocity potential in fluid motion.

Other physical theories which have a similar relation to analytic functions of a complex variable are those of two-dimensional gravitational, electrostatic, and magnetic attractions. In each of these cases a given particle

attracts another with a force directed from the second
particle to the first, of magnitude inversely proportional
to the distance between the particles (not to the square of
the distance as is the case for three-dimensional attractions). Thus if the first particle is at the origin and the
second is at the point whose polar co-ordinates are (r, θ),
or (x, y) in rectangular co-ordinates, the attracting force
F is directed toward the origin, and its magnitude is k/r
where k is not a function of the co-ordinates. Its components F_x and F_y are $-(k \cos \theta)/r$ and $-(k \sin \theta)/r$. But
if we write $u = -k \log r$ we have

$$\frac{\partial u}{\partial x} = F_x \,, \qquad \frac{\partial u}{\partial y} = F_y \,, \qquad \frac{\partial^2 u}{\partial x^2} + \frac{\partial^2 u}{\partial y^2} = 0 \,.$$

The function u is called a *logarithmic potential*.

To find the components of attraction on a point in a
plane due to a body considered as concentrated on a two-
dimensional region of that plane we take the limits of
sums of components of attraction due to small parts of the
body and thus express the total components of attraction
as double integrals. It can be shown that here also there
is a *logarithmic potential function u* such that its partial
derivatives give the components of the attractive force as
above. Further, in all these cases, u satisfies Laplace's
equation, and again we are in contact with the theory of
analytic functions of a complex variable.

Such considerations suggest the interrelations of these
physical problems with each other, and with the geometrical problem of conformal mapping, while complex
variable methods are clearly indicated as desirable for
their mathematical treatment. It is also true that a

physical situation may throw light on a mathematical problem. To give but a single illustration, suppose a flat metal plate to be so insulated that there is no loss of heat by radiation or otherwise from its flat surfaces. Its edges are to be kept at a temperature u such that u has a given value at each point (x, y) of the edge, but u does not depend on the time t. A steady flow goes on in the plate. Physically we feel sure that there is thereby determined one and only one temperature function $u(x, y)$, having a definite value for each point of the plate. We are here answering the mathematical question, a difficult one to solve by purely mathematical methods, whether there exists one and only one function u harmonic throughout a given region and having a preassigned value at each point of the boundary of the region. Thus the one and only harmonic function having the value $\cos\theta$ at each point of the unit circle about the origin is $u = x$. An analogous question for functions of a complex variable will be taken up in the next chapter.

34. **References.** *Osgood's* Chapter VI, pages 230–76, covers the ground of the present chapter, with the exception of physical applications. The latter are discussed in Chapter XIII, which contains an extended development of the properties of the logarithmic potential. The part of Chapter VI relating to conformal mapping is supplemented by Chapter II, section 7. A detailed treatment of linear transformations occupies the last four sections of Chapter VI.

Burkhardt-Rasor devotes Chapter II to rational functions and the conformal maps associated with them, especially stressing linear transformations. Chapter IV contains, in pages 182–88, a general discussion of conformal representation. Physical applications are hardly more than mentioned (pp. 185–88).

Townsend's Chapter IV is on elementary functions and their conformal mapping, and Chapter V discusses linear transformations. In Chapter III, pages 96–98, are a few remarks on physical applications.

In *Goursat-Hedrick* will be found no special treatment of linear transformations or of physical applications. Pages 42–59 are devoted to the general subject of conformal representation.

A similar brevity on certain topics will be noted in *Pierpont*. Linear transformations and conformal mapping receive little space. The later chapters develop properties of functions much used in mathematical physics, but little is said regarding the physical problems themselves. In connection with curve integrals (pp. 153–62), some applications are indicated.

In *Wilson* the reader may consult pages 132–33, 477, 490–91, for a brief treatment of conformal representation. Problems of mathematical physics are treated in various places, especially in Chapter XX.

CHAPTER VI

INTEGRALS OF ANALYTIC FUNCTIONS

35. Indefinite and definite integrals. Following the familiar terminology of elementary calculus we define an indefinite integral of a single-valued continuous function of a complex variable $f(z)$ as a function $F(z)$ whose derivative is $f(z)$. Thus the two following identities are equivalent:

$$F(z) = \int f(z)dz \ , \qquad \frac{dF(z)}{dz} = f(z) \ .$$

With real functions of a real variable, *every* single-valued continuous function has an indefinite integral, but the corresponding statement is not true for functions of a complex variable. For example, $x - iy$ is a continuous function of z which has no indefinite integral. For if there were a function $w = u + iv$ whose derivative is $x - iy$ we would have

$$\frac{dw}{dz} = \frac{\partial w}{\partial x} = \frac{\partial u}{\partial x} + i\frac{\partial v}{\partial x} = x - iy \ ,$$

or

$$\frac{\partial u}{\partial x} = x \ , \qquad \frac{\partial v}{\partial x} = -y \ .$$

If we use the Cauchy-Riemann equation (p. 48),

$$\frac{\partial v}{\partial x} = -\frac{\partial u}{\partial y} \ ,$$

the last pair of equations above becomes

$$\frac{\partial u}{\partial x} = x \ , \qquad \frac{\partial u}{\partial y} = y \ .$$

By differentiating these equations we see that

$$\frac{\partial^2 u}{\partial x^2} + \frac{\partial^2 u}{\partial y^2} = 2 \ ,$$

so that u does not satisfy Laplace's equation (p. 50) and cannot be the real part of a function w that has a derivative. It follows that no function w has the derivative $x - iy$.

We shall see later in this chapter that if $F(z)$ has the derivative $f(z)$, then $f(z)$ is also analytic. It is only analytic functions which have indefinite integrals. In the example just given, $x - iy$ is not analytic.

The formal parallelism which we have already so often observed between formulas and definitions for functions of a real variable on the one hand, and functions of a complex variable on the other, suggests that the definite integral from z_0 to Z_0 of a continuous function $f(z)$ be defined as the limit of the sum

$$S = f(z_1)\Delta z_1 + f(z_2)\Delta z_2 + \ \cdot \ \cdot \ \cdot \ \cdot \ + f(z_n)\Delta z_n \ ,$$

where for each subscript k, the symbol Δz_k stands for $z_k - z_{k-1}$, and $z_n = Z_0$. This brings up first the question of how we are to take the sequence of points $z_0, z_1, \ . \ . \ . \ . \ ,$ z_{n-1}, Z_0. To limit these points to the straight line from z_0 to Z_0 would have decided disadvantages when we wish later to consider the upper limit of integration as variable. If they lie on a curve segment C extending from z_0 to Z_0, the limit of the foregoing sum, suitably defined, is called the *curve integral of $f(z)$ along C*. As with real curve integrals we then wish to find a condition that the curve integral of $f(z)$ be the same for every path from z_0 to Z_0 lying in a given region T_1 whose boundary is a single closed curve. We shall find that this condition is that $f(z)$ be analytic throughout the region.

The properties of the definite integral have been developed directly from the foregoing definition by various writers. By this means Goursat succeeded in proving that if $f(z)$ is analytic throughout a region T_1, in the sense of having a finite derivative at each point of T_1, its integral between two points of T_1 is independent of the path. Previously such a proof had been carried through only with additional hypotheses regarding the continuity of the derivative of $f(z)$. Here we shall follow the older way of expressing the complex integral in terms of real curve integrals.

If we use the familiar u, v notation, the sum above becomes

$$S = [u(x_1, y_1) + iv(x_1, y_1)][\Delta x_1 + i\Delta y_1]$$
$$+ [u(x_2, y_2) + iv(x_2, y_2)][\Delta x_2 + i\Delta y_2] + \cdots$$
$$+ [u(x_n, y_n) + iv(x_n, y_n)][\Delta x_n + i\Delta y_n] .$$

If we separate real from pure imaginary terms this breaks up into the sums

$$[u(x_1, y_1)\Delta x_1 + u(x_2, y_2)\Delta x_2 + \cdots + u(x_n, y_n)\Delta x_n]$$
$$- [v(x_1, y_1)\Delta y_1 + v(x_2, y_2)\Delta y_2 + \cdots + v(x_n, y_n)\Delta y_n] ,$$

and

$$i[v(x_1, y_1)\Delta x_1 + v(x_2, y_2)\Delta x_2 + \cdots + v(x_n, y_n)\Delta x_n]$$
$$+ i[u(x_1, y_1)\Delta y_1 + u(x_2, y_2)\Delta y_2 + \cdots + u(x_n, y_n)\Delta y_n] ,$$

whose limits define certain curve integrals. We thus arrive at the formula

$$(1) \quad \int_C f(z)dz = \int_C (u + iv)(dx + idy)$$
$$= \int_C (udx - vdy) + i\int_C (vdx + udy) ,$$

the last sum of integrals being what we would get by formally multiplying $u+iv$ by $dx+idy$ and expressing the integral of the result as a sum of integrals. If u and v are single valued and have continuous first partial derivatives throughout a closed *simply connected* region T_1, i.e., one whose boundary is a single connected closed curve that does not cut itself, then necessary and sufficient conditions that each of these integrals have the same value for all paths in T_1 with the same end-points are obtained from the criterion of page 37 which states that

$$\int_C Pdx+Qdy$$

is independent of the path if $\partial Q/\partial x = \partial P/\partial y$. The application of this test to the two last integrals in formula (1) gives

$$\frac{\partial u}{\partial x}=\frac{\partial v}{\partial y}\,,\qquad \frac{\partial u}{\partial y}=-\frac{\partial v}{\partial x}\,;$$

i.e., *the Cauchy-Riemann equations are satisfied by u and v at every point of T_1.* But with the hypotheses made on u and v, the statement that the Cauchy-Riemann equations are satisfied is equivalent to saying that $f(z)$ is analytic at each point of T_1.

Thus if $f(z)$ is analytic we may write its integral from z_0 to Z_0 without ambiguity in the form

$$\int_{z_0}^{Z_0} f(z)dz\,,$$

the path of integration from z_0 to Z_0 being immaterial so long as it lies within the region T_1.

36. Formulas for definite integrals. It can easily be shown that the integral thus defined satisfies many of the formulas for real integrals. For instance, we have

$$\int_{z_0}^{Z_0} (f(z)+\phi(z)\,)dz = \int_{z_0}^{Z_0} f(z)dz + \int_{z_0}^{Z_0} \phi(z)dz \ ,$$

$$\int_{z_0}^{Z_0} k\,f(z)dz = k \int_{z_0}^{Z_0} f(z)dz \ ,$$

$$\int_{z_0}^{z_1} f(z)dz + \int_{z_1}^{z_2} f(z)dz = \int_{z_0}^{z_2} f(z)dz \ ,$$

$$\int_{z_0}^{z_0} f(z)dz = 0 \ ,$$

with the corollary that the integral of $f(z)$ from z_0 to Z_0 is the negative of the integral from Z_0 to z_0. To this list we may add the formula which shows that the integral from z_0 to z is a value of the indefinite integral. In fact, if we write

$$F(z) = \int_{z_0}^{z} f(z)dz = U + iV$$

$$= \int_{(x_0, y_0)}^{(x,\ y)} (udx - vdy) + i \int_{(x_0,\ y)}^{(x,\ y)} (vdx + udy) \ ,$$

we have, from page 37,

$$\frac{\partial U}{\partial x} = u \ , \qquad \frac{\partial U}{\partial y} = -v \ ,$$

$$\frac{\partial V}{\partial x} = v \ , \qquad \frac{\partial V}{\partial y} = u \ .$$

We thus see at once that U and V verify the Cauchy-Riemann equations, so that $F(z)$ is analytic and its derivative is given by the formula

$$(2) \qquad \frac{dF(z)}{dz} = \frac{\partial F}{\partial x} = \frac{\partial U}{\partial x} + i \frac{\partial V}{\partial x} = u + iv = f(z) \ .$$

It can be shown, as in real integration, that the most general formula for the indefinite integral is $F(z) +$ constant.

The result expressed by formula (2) is so important that we restate it here:

The integral

$$F(z) = \int_{z_0}^{z} f(z) dz$$

is analytic throughout every simply connected region T_1 within which $f(z)$ is analytic, and its derivative is $f(z)$.

A useful inequality is derived from the sum S whose limit we first considered in defining the integral. Since the absolute value of a sum is not greater than the sum of the absolute values of its terms, the absolute value of S is less than or equal to the sum whose typical term is $|f(z_i)| \cdot \sqrt{(\Delta x_i)^2 + (\Delta y_i)^2}$. When we pass to the limit, this gives the inequality

$$\left| \int_C f(z) dz \right| \leq \int_C |f(z)| \, |dz| = \int_C |f(z)| \, ds \ .$$

If no value on C of the continuous real function $|f(z)|$ is greater than a positive constant M, and the length of C is l, a familiar theorem for real integrals states that the last integral above is not greater than the integral in which M

replaces the integrand. The result is expressed by the formula

(3)
$$\left| \int_C f(z)dz \right| \leq Ml ,$$

and here $f(z)$ need not even be analytic.

We shall state without proof two properties of integrals with a parameter. Let $z = x + iy$ and $t = \xi + i\eta$ be two complex variables, and let

$$\phi(z, t) = u(x, y, \xi, \eta) + iv(x, y, \xi, \eta)$$

be a single-valued function continuous in its two complex variables when z is any point of a region T in the z-plane, and t is any point of a curve segment C of that plane. By this we mean that u and v are continuous functions of their four variables for that region and curve. *Then*

$$\Phi(z) = \int_C \phi(z, t)dt$$

is a single-valued continuous function of z throughout T. If, further, $\phi(z, t)$ is an analytic function of z within T, then $\Phi(z)$ is also analytic within T, and

$$\frac{d}{dz} \Phi(z) = \int_C \frac{\partial}{\partial z} \phi(z, t)dt .$$

37. Remarks concerning the evaluation of complex integrals. In the evaluation of complex integrals we have, of course, the expedient in every case of reduction to ordinary curve integrals. Thus

$$\int_{z_0}^{Z} z^2 dz = \int_{(x_0, y_0)}^{(X, Y)} [(x^2 - y^2)dx - 2xydy]$$
$$+ i \int_{(x_0, y_0)}^{(X, Y)} [2xydx + (x^2 - y^2)dy] ,$$

and, since both integrals are independent of the path, we may evaluate these by an elbow path from (x_0, y_0) to (X, y_0), and thence to (X, Y). The expression to the right thus becomes

$$\int_{x_0}^{X}(x^2-y_0^2)dx-\int_{y_0}^{Y}2Xy\,dy+i\int_{x_0}^{X}2xy_0\,dx+i\int_{y_0}^{Y}(X^2-y^2)dy$$

$$=\left(\frac{X^3}{3}-\frac{x_0^3}{3}-XY^2+x_0y_0^2\right)+i\left(X^2Y-x_0^2y_0-\frac{Y^3}{3}+\frac{y_0^3}{3}\right)$$

$$=\tfrac{1}{3}[(X+iY)^3-(x_0+iy_0)^3]=\frac{Z^3}{3}-\frac{z_0^3}{3}.$$

This computation is much shortened by observing that an indefinite integral of z^2 is $z^3/3$, and that the definite integral of an analytic function from z_0 to Z is the difference of values of an indefinite integral at these points. Let us be watchful, however, in the use of this principle. Consider the integral

$$\int_C \frac{1}{z}\,dz,$$

where C is any closed curve that does not cut itself, to which the origin is interior. An indefinite integral is $\log z$, and we might conclude that when we start and finish our path of integration at the same point z_0 the value of the integral would be $\log z_0 - \log z_0 = 0$. However, our connection between the definite and indefinite integral depended on our restriction of paths of integration to a *simply connected* region throughout which $f(z)$ is analytic. For the function $1/z$, a circular ring about the origin is a region, though not a simply connected one, throughout which it is analytic, and we now consider such a ring to which all points of C are interior. By a cut across the ring from one boundary to another, we convert our region into a simply connected region T_1 for which we may define infinitely many *branches* of log z so that each is single valued and analytic in T_1. An indefinite integral is given by any one of these infinitely many branches of log z. But as z makes a circuit of the origin, each branch of the logarithm of z increases by $2\pi i$. Hence the values of the branch of log z that we have chosen as our indefinite integral differ

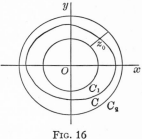

Fig. 16

from each other by $2\pi i$ when a point z_0 on the cut is approached from one side or the other, and our definite integral around C is thus equal to the difference, $2\pi i$.

A similar argument, when C is a closed curve that does not cut itself and has z_0 within it, gives the formulas

$$(4) \qquad \int_C \frac{dt}{(t-z_0)} = 2\pi i \, ,$$

$$\int_C \frac{dt}{(t-z_0)^{m+1}} = 0 \, , \; m = \pm 1 \, , \; \pm 2 \, , \cdots \cdot .$$

This result could also be obtained as follows if we take C as a circle of radius r and center at z_0. From a remark at the close of the next section it follows that integration on such a circle gives the same result as integration on any other curve C as specified above. For t on this circle we have

$$t - z_0 = r(\cos \phi + i \sin \phi) = re^{i\phi}, \quad dt = ire^{i\phi}d\phi ,$$

$$\int_C \frac{dt}{(t-z_0)^{m+1}} = \int_0^{2\pi} ir^{-m}e^{-im\phi}d\phi$$

$$= ir^{-m} \int_0^{2\pi} (\cos m\phi - i \sin m\phi)d\phi ,$$

from which we at once obtain the foregoing result. This procedure illustrates an abbreviated form of reduction to ordinary integrals which is equivalent to a reduction through real curve integrals.

38. **Cauchy's integral theorem.** To say, as at the end of section 35, that the integral of a function $f(z)$ analytic with-

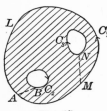

FIG. 17

in the simply connected region T_1 is independent of the path is the same as saying that its integral around any closed path C within the region T_1 is zero. The integral around C will be zero even if we take C as the boundary of T_1 and require merely that $f(z)$ be single-valued and con-

tinuous throughout the *closed* region T_1 and that it be analytic throughout the open region T_1. The reader will recall that a closed region includes its boundaries, while an open one does not. But what if the region T_1 is replaced by a region T which is *not* simply connected, and, instead of being bounded by one closed curve, has an outer boundary C_1, and inner non-intersecting boundaries C_2, C_3, ... , as in Figure 17? In this figure we have shaded the region T and have indicated by arrows on C_1, C_2, C_3 *the positive sense with respect to T*, which is defined as the direction taken by a traveler who keeps T to his left. Now let us introduce the *cross-cuts* AB and MN. The region T_1, whose boundaries are C_1, C_2, C_3, and these cross-cuts, is simply connected and the integral of $f(z)$ around its total boundary is zero. Thus we have, in abbreviated notation,

$$\int_{AM} + \int_{MN} + \int_{C_3} + \int_{NM} + \int_{MLA} + \int_{AB} + \int_{C_2} + \int_{BA} = 0 .$$

Since $f(z)$ is single-valued, the second and fourth of these integrals cancel, as do also the sixth and eighth. The sum of the first and fifth is the integral along C_1. Hence if C indicates the total boundary of T we have

$$\int_{C_1} f(z)dz + \int_{C_2} f(z)dz + \int_{C_3} f(z)dz = \int_C f(z)dz = 0 .$$

The procedure is plain, no matter how many curves make up the boundary C. The result, that the integral of $f(z)$ around C vanishes whether T is simply connected or not, is *Cauchy's integral theorem*, first published in 1825. Another way of stating it is to say that the integral taken positively with respect to T along the outer boundary of C is equal to the sum of the integrals along the inner boundaries taken in the negative sense with respect to T, which is, of course, the positive sense for each with respect to the region within it.

When $f(z)$ is single-valued and analytic throughout a region whose boundaries are a closed curve C_1 and a point z_0 interior to that curve, and is continuous throughout the region, including C_1 but not necessarily including z_0, the expression

$$\frac{1}{2\pi i} \int_{C_1} f(z)dz$$

is what Cauchy styled the *residue* of $f(z)$ at z_0. It follows from Cauchy's integral theorem that if c is a sufficiently small circle about z_0, so that $f(z)$ is analytic throughout the region bounded by C_1 and c, the integral about c is equal to the integral about C_1 and may be substituted for it. These considerations were the foundation of Cauchy's calculus of residues by means of which he investigated many improper real integrals and obtained series and product developments for real functions.

Before passing to the next topic, we remark, without giving a proof, that there is a form in which the converse of Cauchy's integral theorem is true. This converse, called Morera's theorem, states that if $f(z)$ is single-valued and continuous throughout a region T and the integral of $f(z)$ vanishes when taken over any closed curve whatever within T, then $f(z)$ is analytic throughout T.

39. Cauchy's integral formula. We have already investigated the integral with respect to t of $1/(t-z_0)$ around a closed curve C about z_0 and have obtained its value in formula (4). A generalization that at once suggests itself is a treatment of the integral

$$\int_C \frac{f(t)}{t-z}\,dt \,,$$

where $f(t)$ is continuous for all values of t on the boundary C of a closed region T to which z is interior. If we like, T may be a multiply connected region, i.e., a region with holes, provided C is then its entire boundary, the integration over each boundary curve being positive with respect to T. The integrand is a continuous function of t and the parameter z for t on C and z in the open region T, and is an analytic function of z throughout open T, hence, according to the statement of page 89, the integral represents a function of z analytic throughout open T.

When $f(t)$ is a polynomial it is easy to show that the foregoing integral divided by $2\pi i$ is equal to $f(z)$. This follows from a well-known theorem of algebra that $f(t) - f(z)$ is divisible by $t - z$, the quotient being a polynomial in t. Since a polynomial is everywhere analytic, its integral around C is zero, by Cauchy's integral theorem. Thus we have

$$\frac{1}{2\pi i}\int_C \frac{f(t) - f(z)}{t - z}\, dt = 0\ ,$$

$$\frac{1}{2\pi i}\int_C \frac{f(t)}{t - z}\, dt = \frac{1}{2\pi i}\int_C \frac{f(z)}{t - z}\, dt = \frac{f(z)}{2\pi i}\int_C \frac{dt}{t - z} = f(z)\ .$$

The foregoing result,

$$(5)\qquad\qquad f(z) = \frac{1}{2\pi i}\int_C \frac{f(t)}{t - z}\, dt\ ,$$

is called *Cauchy's integral formula*. We will now show that it is valid for every function $f(z)$ that is single-valued and continuous throughout the closed region T and analytic throughout open T. This will follow, as for the case where $f(z)$ was taken as a polynomial, if we can prove that

$$\int_C \frac{f(t) - f(z)}{t - z}\, dt = 0\ .$$

Let us observe in the first place that the foregoing integral has a value that is constant when z is fixed. If we can show that its absolute value is less than any assignable positive real number η, then the constant value of the foregoing integral for fixed z can be nothing else but zero.

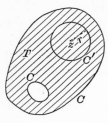

FIG. 18

If we now draw a circle C' of radius r, with z as a center, and take r so small that the closed region within this circle is interior to T, then C together with C' forms the boundary of a region T' within which our integrand is analytic, and the counter-clockwise integral over C plus the clockwise integral over C' will be zero; or, if we take the latter counterclockwise and so change its sign,

$$\int_C \frac{f(t)-f(z)}{t-z}\,dt = \int_{C'} \frac{f(t)-f(z)}{t-z}\,dt\ .$$

But we have

$$\lim_{t=z} \frac{f(t)-f(z)}{t-z} = \frac{d}{dz}f(z) = f'(z)\ .$$

Hence

$$\frac{f(t)-f(z)}{t-z} = f'(z)+\zeta\ ,$$

where ζ is a continuous function of t whose absolute value can be made less than any particular positive constant η_1, no matter how small, for all t such that $|\,t-z\,|$ is sufficiently small. Hence we have

$$\int_{C'} \frac{f(t)-f(z)}{t-z}\,dt = \int_{C'} f'(z)dt + \int_{C'} \zeta dt$$

$$= f'(z)\int_{C'} dt + \int_{C'} \zeta dt$$

$$= \int_{C'} \zeta dt\ .$$

But if r is sufficiently small the absolute value of this last expression is, by formula (3), page 89, less than $\eta_1 l$, where l is the length of the circumference C'. If, then, the radius of this circle is sufficiently small, we can take $\eta_1 l$ less than η and our argument is thus complete.

40. **Some immediate consequences of Cauchy's integral formula.** From formula (5) are derived many fundamental properties of analytic functions. One of these is connected with the observation that the integral is concerned only with values of $f(t)$ on the boundary C. There is, then, one and only one function $f(z)$ which is single-valued and continuous in closed T, analytic throughout open T, and which has a given value at each point of the boundary, the set of boundary values being one that can be assumed by such a function. To put it briefly, *an analytic function is uniquely determined by its boundary values*, just as is the temperature function in the flow of heat.

Note, however, that we do not say that any continuous set of boundary values whatever can be used instead of $f(t)$ in the integrand and that the integral will then be a function which is continuous in the *closed* region T and has the given values on the boundary; the function generated is analytic in the *open* region T, nevertheless. For example, if $t = \xi + i\eta$, the function $\bar{t} = \xi - i\eta$ is everywhere continuous. On the unit circle we have

$$t = e^{+i\theta}\ , \quad \frac{1}{t} = e^{-i\theta}\ , \qquad \bar{t} = e^{-i\theta}\ ,$$

which incidentally gives an example of two functions, $1/t$ and $\bar{t}$, *not* everywhere analytic in a region T, that are equal along the boundary C, contrary to what we have seen is the case for functions analytic throughout T and continuous in closed T. If C is the unit circle and z is an interior point, we have, if z is not the origin,

$$
\begin{aligned}
\frac{1}{2\pi i}\int_C \frac{\bar{t}}{t-z}\,dt &= \frac{1}{2\pi i}\int_C \frac{dt}{t(t-z)} \\
&= \frac{1}{2\pi i}\int_C \frac{1}{z}\left(\frac{1}{t-z}-\frac{1}{t}\right)dt \\
&= \frac{1}{2\pi iz}\left[\int_C \frac{dt}{t-z}-\int_C \frac{dt}{t-0}\right] \\
&= \frac{1}{2\pi iz}\,[2\pi i-2\pi i]=0\;,
\end{aligned}
$$

and the same result holds when $z=0$. The function 0 is analytic, but does not take on the boundary values $e^{-i\theta}$.

A particularly interesting consequence is that if $f(z)$ is analytic throughout an open region T, then its derivatives of all orders exist at each point of T, and each of them is thus also analytic throughout T. In fact, if we take C as a closed curve about z inclosing a region which, with its boundary, lies within T, the integral on the right side of Cauchy's formula admits differentiation under the integral sign, according to the theorem of page 89 regarding integrals with a parameter. Thus

$$
f'(z) = \frac{1}{2\pi i}\int_C \frac{\partial}{\partial z}\frac{f(t)}{t-z}\,dt = \frac{1}{2\pi i}\int_C \frac{f(t)}{(t-z)^2}\,dt\;,
$$

and the new integral may be differentiated similarly. In this way we obtain the formula for the second derivative

$$
f''(z) = \frac{2}{2\pi i}\int_C \frac{f(t)}{(t-z)^3}\,dt\;,
$$

and for the nth derivative

$$(6) \qquad f^{(n)}(z) = \frac{n!}{2\pi i} \int_C \frac{f(t)}{(t-z)^{n+1}} \, dt.$$

It follows that if $f(z) = u + iv$, both u and v have partial derivatives of all orders throughout T. This remarkable property is by no means shared by all real functions that have partial derivatives of the first order. The function $\phi(x)$, for example, whose value is x^2 when x is *positive*, and is 0 for all other values of x, has a continuous first derivative with respect to x, but no second derivative with respect to x at the origin.

From the foregoing formula (6) for $f^{(n)}(z)$ we obtain a relation which is called *Cauchy's inequality* as follows. Let C be a circle of radius r with center at z, and M be a constant not exceeded by any value of $|f(z)|$ on C. Then from formula (3), since the absolute value of the integrand in (6) is less than M/r^{n+1} for all values of t on C, we have

$$(7) \qquad |f^{(n)}(z)| \leqq \frac{n!}{2\pi} \frac{M}{r^{n+1}} \cdot 2\pi r = (n!)\frac{M}{r^n}.$$

This formula is valid for $f^{(0)}(z) \equiv f(z)$ if we take $n!$ as 1 when $n = 0$, and in this case shows that the absolute value of a function analytic throughout a region T cannot have a greater value at an interior point z than its greatest value on a circle about z which, with the region bounded by it, is interior to T. It follows that $|f(z)|$ cannot have a maximum at z.

Another interesting consequence of Cauchy's inequality is Liouville's theorem which states that *no function except a constant can be analytic everywhere and finite.* When we say that a function is everywhere finite we mean that there is a real constant M such that for all values of z we have $|f(z)| < M$. As an example of the applications of this theorem note that e^z is analytic everywhere, but cannot be everywhere finite since it is not constant. We prove Liouville's theorem by taking $n = 1$ in Cauchy's inequality (7), and observing that we can now take the same M no matter how large r is. Thus $f'(z)$, when z has been fixed, has a constant absolute value less than M/r, which can be given as small a positive value as we please by taking r sufficiently large. It follows that $f'(z) = 0$ for every value of z. Now one value of the indefinite integral of $f'(z)$ is $f(z)$, and *every* indefinite integral is therefore of form $f(z) +$ constant, according to our statement on page 88. On the other hand, an indefinite integral of $f'(z) = 0$ is 0 itself. Hence we have

$$f(z) + \text{constant} = 0 ,$$

or in other words $f(z)$ is constant.

At this stage, nothing is more likely to convince one of the power of the methods here developed than the following proof of what is called the *fundamental theorem of algebra*. This theorem states that if $f(z)$ is any polynomial of degree greater than zero, with coefficients that are real or complex, then the equation $f(z) = 0$ has at least one root. This is a difficult theorem to prove by purely algebraic methods. But if $f(z)$ were zero for *no* value of z, its reciprocal would be everywhere analytic and finite. The last statement follows from the fact that the limit of $1/f(z)$ as z becomes infinite is zero. Hence if we take a sufficiently large circle about the origin there is a positive constant m_1 such that at every outside point the absolute value of $1/f(z)$ is less than m_1, while $1/f(z)$ is continuous on and within the circle, and so its absolute value has a maximum m for all points on or inside the circle. Thus Liouville's theorem would apply, and the reciprocal of $f(z)$ would be a constant, which it is not if $f(z)$ is of degree greater than zero. Thus our hypothesis that $f(z)$ vanishes for no z must be false.

It might seem that the foregoing proof applies to equations $f(z) = 0$ of a more general sort, where $f(z)$ is not a polynomial but is everywhere analytic. The example of the function e^z which vanishes for no value of z would shake one's faith in such an extension. Our proof required that $1/f(z)$ be finite outside a sufficiently large circle, and it is known that among single-valued functions $f(z)$ everywhere analytic only polynomials have this property.

41. Taylor's theorem with remainder. With functions of a real variable much stress is laid on expanding functions in Taylor's series

$$f(x) = f(a) + f'(a)(x-a) + \frac{f'(a)}{2!}(x-a)^2 + \cdots \cdots$$
$$+ \frac{f^{(n)}(a)}{n!}(x-a)^n + \cdots \cdots .$$

A proof of the validity of such an expansion depends on showing that the difference between $f(x)$ and the sum of the first n terms of the series approaches zero, for each value of x under consideration, when n becomes infinite. In spite of general formulas that exist for this difference, or *remainder*, the problem of showing that it approaches zero as n becomes infinite may be very difficult. The analogous question for analytic functions of a complex variable is much easier to handle.

Let us take T as a region interior to a region throughout which $f(z)$ is single-valued and analytic; let the boundary of T be C, and let z and a be interior to T. We start with Cauchy's integral formula and transform it as follows:

$$f(z) = \frac{1}{2\pi i} \int_C \frac{f(t)}{t-z}\, dt$$

$$= \frac{1}{2\pi i} \int_C \frac{f(t)}{(t-a)} \left[\frac{1}{1 - \dfrac{z-a}{t-a}} \right] dt \; .$$

To the expression within brackets the algebraic identity

$$\frac{1}{1-x} = 1 + x + x^2 + \cdots \cdots + x^{n-1} + \frac{x^n}{1-x}$$

can be applied, and this gives us

$$\frac{1}{1 - \dfrac{z-a}{t-a}} = 1 + \frac{z-a}{t-a} + \left(\frac{z-a}{t-a}\right)^2 + \cdots \cdots + \left(\frac{z-a}{t-a}\right)^{n-1}$$

$$+ \frac{(z-a)^n}{(t-a)^{n-1}\,(t-z)} \; .$$

If this expression is used in the last integral above, and the result is written as a sum of integrals, we have

$$f(z) = \frac{1}{2\pi i} \int_C \frac{f(t)}{t-a}\, dt + (z-a)\, \frac{1}{2\pi i} \int_C \frac{f(t)}{(t-a)^2}\, dt$$

$$+ (z-a)^2\, \frac{1}{2\pi i} \int_C \frac{f(t)}{(t-a)^3}\, dt + \cdots \cdots$$

$$+ (z-a)^{n-1} \frac{1}{2\pi i} \int_C \frac{f(t)}{(t-a)^n}\, dt$$

$$+ (z-a)^n\, \frac{1}{2\pi i} \int_C \frac{f(t)}{(t-a)^n(t-z)}\, dt \; .$$

The first n of these integrals are readily expressed, by means of formulas (5) and (6), in terms of $f(a)$ and the successive derivatives of $f(z)$ at a. We thus obtain *Taylor's theorem with remainder*

$$(8) \quad f(z) = f(a) + f'(a)(z-a) + \frac{f''(a)}{2!}(z-a)^2 + \cdots$$
$$+ \frac{f^{(n-1)}(a)}{(n-1)!}(z-a)^{n-1} + R_n ,$$

where the remainder R_n has the form

$$(9) \qquad R_n = (z-a)^n P_n(z) ,$$

and $P_n(z)$ is the function, analytic throughout open T,

$$(10) \qquad P_n(z) = \frac{1}{2\pi i} \int_C \frac{f(t)}{(t-a)^n(t-z)} \, dt .$$

An inequality for $P_n(z)$ may be obtained by taking two concentric circles C_1 and C_2, of radii r_1 and r_2 and center a, such that $r_1 > r_2$ and the outer circle, together with the region within it, is interior to T. Then, by Cauchy's integral theorem, the integral that figures in the expression for $P_n(z)$ is the same when C is replaced by C_1 provided z is within C_1. If we add the hypoth-

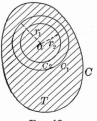

Fig. 19

esis that z is also within C_2, we have for values of t on C_1,

$$|t-a| = r_1 , \qquad |t-z| > r_1 - r_2 , \qquad f(t) \le M ,$$

where M is the maximum of $f(t)$ on C_1. We thus have from formula (3), page 89,

$$|P_n(z)| \le \frac{1}{2\pi} \frac{M}{r_1^n(r_1-r_2)} 2\pi r_1 = \frac{M}{r_1^{n-1}(r_1-r_2)} .$$

But for z within C_2 the absolute value of $(z-a)$ is less than r_2, and hence

$$| R_n | = | z-a |^n | P_n(z) | < \frac{Mr_2^n}{r_1^{n-1}(r_1-r_2)} = M \frac{r_2}{r_1-r_2}\left(\frac{r_2}{r_1}\right)^{n-1}.$$

Since r_1 is greater than r_2 it follows that *for every z within C_2 the limit of R_n is zero when n becomes infinite.*

A classic example to show that the corresponding theorem is not true for all real functions of a real variable, or even for all that have derivatives of all orders for every value of the variable, is given by the function e^{-1/x^2}, defined so as to have the value zero for $x=0$. If we take a as the point $x=0$, this function vanishes at a, and it can be shown that all its derivatives vanish at a. Hence in Taylor's theorem with remainder all terms on the right vanish except R_n itself, which is equal therefore to the function and does not vary with n. Obviously, then, its value does not approach zero as n becomes infinite. If, however, a function of the complex variable is analytic throughout a neighborhood of a real point $z=a$ and is real when z is replaced by the real variable x, then our argument can be carried over to the real function of x, which is also called *analytic*, and it will follow that its Taylor's remainder will also approach zero as n becomes infinite provided x is in a sufficiently small interval extending to each side of a.

In the next chapter we shall consider the Taylor's series obtained by letting n become infinite, and, in the customary way, develop certain properties of analytic functions thereby. Nearly all of these could, however, be obtained by use of Taylor's theorem with remainder.

42. **References.** Page references for the topics espe-

cially considered in this chapter are as follows: *Osgood*, pages 277–308, 316–19; *Goursat-Hedrick*, pages 60–77, 81, 96–109; *Burkhardt-Rasor*, pages 188–99; *Pierpont*, pages 186–97, 211–16; *Townsend*, pages 60–82, 89–92; *Wilson*, pages 292, 300, 302–5, 477, 482.

Proofs of Morera's theorem will be found in *Osgood*, pages 302–3; *Goursat-Hedrick*, page 78; *Townsend*, pages 80–82. The Goursat proof of Cauchy's integral theorem is given in *Osgood*, pages 349–52; *Goursat-Hedrick*, pages 66–70; *Burkhardt-Rasor*, pages 190–91 (with a reference to pp. 160–62); *Townsend*, pages 66–70.

Residues are treated in *Osgood*, pages 331–34; *Goursat-Hedrick*, pages 94–95; *Burkhardt-Rasor*, pages 236–45; *Pierpont*, pages 256–59; *Townsend*, pages 284–89. Examples of the calculation of real improper integrals by the method of residues are given in *Osgood*, pages 289–95; *Goursat-Hedrick*, pages 97–101; *Townsend*, page 289.

CHAPTER VII

INFINITE SERIES

43. Convergence and divergence. In every book on the calculus there will be found at least a brief treatment of infinite series of real numbers or functions. Such a series being defined as an array of the form

$$u_0 + u_1 + u_2 + \cdots + u_n + \cdots ,$$

where the nth term is given by some formula, we designate by s_n the sum of the first n terms for each positive integer n, and consider the sequence

$$s_1, s_2, \ldots , s_n, \ldots$$

If this sequence has a limit U as n becomes infinite, i.e., if

$$\lim_{n=\infty} s_n = U ,$$

the series is said to be *convergent*, otherwise it is *divergent*. In the former case it is sometimes said to have the *sum* or *value U*, or with a less exact phraseology, to be equal to U.

These definitions we may carry over bodily to series of complex numbers or functions. Let us write, for each n,

$$u_n = a_n + i\beta_n , \qquad s_n = s_n(a) + i s_n(\beta) ,$$

where $s_n(a)$ denotes the sum of the first n of the a's, and similarly for $s_n(\beta)$. Then, in accordance with the statement concerning limits on page 45, s_n has a limit if and only if $s_n(a)$ and $s_n(\beta)$ both have limits. Thus the question of the convergence of a complex series is reduced to that of the series of real parts of its terms and that of the series of coefficients of i.

For present purposes it will be sufficient to quote three tests for the convergence of series of real numbers. The first, called the *comparison test*, states that if no term is negative and if each term is less than or equal to the corresponding term of a second series with no negative terms which is convergent, then the first series is convergent. If we replace the words "less than" by "greater than," and the word "convergent" by "divergent," we have the comparison test for divergence. A corollary is the *ratio test*, which states that if the limit as n becomes infinite of the absolute value of the test-ratio u_{n+1}/u_n exists and is less than 1 the series is convergent, and if it is greater than 1 the series is divergent. Finally there is the theorem that a series having positive and negative terms converges if it is *absolutely convergent*, i.e., if the *absolute-value* series

$$| u_0 | + | u_1 | + | u_2 | + \cdots + | u_n | + \cdots$$

is convergent.

The third of these tests at once suggests the question whether it can be extended to the case where the numbers u_n are complex. The answer is affirmative, for when $u_n = a_n + i\beta_n$ we have $| a_n | \leq | u_n |$, and similarly for $| \beta_n |$, so that the absolute-value series for the u's is a comparison series for those of the a's and the β's. Thus if the series of absolute values of the u's converges the a-series and the β-series are both convergent, and the u-series must also be convergent. It should be noted that the convergence of the absolute-value series is sufficient, but not necessary, for the convergence of the u-series.

44. Power series.

When we consider a series of functions and write

$$F(z) = f_0(z) + f_1(z) + f_2(z) + \cdots + f_n(z) + \cdots ,$$

we define the value of $F(z)$ at a point z_0 as the sum or value of the infinite series when z_0 is substituted for z, provided this series is then convergent. An especially important class of series of functions is that of the *power series*

$$(1) \qquad c_0 + c_1 z + c_2 z^2 + \cdots + c_n z^n + \cdots ,$$

where the coefficients c are constants. Sometimes the series in which $(z - z_0)$ replaces z is also given this name; its discussion reduces to that of the foregoing series if we make the transformation $Z = z - z_0$.

A power series (1) may converge for no value of z except $z = 0$, and there are power series that converge for all values of z, but with the exception of these two cases there is always a circle about the origin, called the *circle of convergence*, such that the series converges at every inner point and diverges at every outer point. On the circle there may be points at which it converges, and others at which it diverges. For example, the series

$$z - \frac{z^2}{2} + \frac{z^3}{3} - \frac{z^4}{4} + \cdots$$

converges absolutely, by the ratio test, for every z within the unit circle, and diverges for every z outside it, but for $z = 1$ it is convergent, and for $z = -1$ it is divergent. The argument in the general case is this: If a series (1) converges for $z = Z$, where $Z \neq 0$, there must be a positive constant G which is greater than every term of the absolute-value series in Z

$$| c_0 |+| c_1 | \, | Z |+| c_2 | \, | Z |^2+ \cdots + | c_n | \, | Z |^n+ \cdots ;$$

otherwise, no matter how far out we went, the values of s_n for the original series (1) with Z substituted for z would not be clustering around a limiting value. The absolute-value series of (1) may be written

$$| c_0 |+| c_1 | \cdot | Z | \cdot \left| \frac{z}{Z} \right|+| c_2 | \cdot | Z |^2 \left| \frac{z}{Z} \right|^2$$

$$+ \cdots + | c_n | \cdot | Z |^n \cdot \left| \frac{z}{Z} \right|^n+ \cdots ,$$

and this is less, term by term, than

$$G+G \left| \frac{z}{Z} \right|+G \left| \frac{z}{Z} \right|^2+ \cdots +G \left| \frac{z}{Z} \right|^n+ \cdots .$$

This last series has $| z |/| Z |$ for its test ratio, and so converges for every z whose absolute value is less than $| Z |$. Thus *if* (1) *converges for a value $z=Z$ it converges absolutely for every z of smaller absolute value than Z*, that is, for every point within a circle whose center is at the origin, and which passes through Z. If the series has a point of divergence $z=\zeta$, all points outside the circle about the origin through the point ζ are points of divergence; for if one outside point were a point of convergence a circle through it about the origin would include only points of convergence and ζ would be within that circle. Let us briefly call a circle with the origin as center and within which the series converges a C-circle and one outside which it diverges a D-circle. Through every point of the plane passes a circle of one sort or the other; within a C-circle there can be only C-circles and outside a D-circle there are only D-circles. It follows that there is one and only one circle common to both classes, the circle of convergence.

It can be shown that if we form new series from (1) by integrating or differentiating each term, these new series will have the same circle of convergence as (1).

An interesting connection between power series and the real trigonometric series so important in mathematical physics appears if we write

$$z = re^{i\theta}, \qquad c_n = |c_n| e^{i\gamma_n}.$$

The $(n+1)$th term of (1) then takes the form

$$|c_n| e^{i\gamma_n} r^n e^{in\theta} = |c_n| r^n e^{i(\gamma_n + n\theta)}$$
$$= |c_n| r^n [\cos(\gamma_n + n\theta) + i \sin(\gamma_n + n\theta)],$$

and the real part of this is

$$|c_n| r^n \cos \gamma_n \cos n\theta - |c_n| r^n \sin \gamma_n \sin n\theta,$$

with a similar expression for the coefficient of i. A trigonometric series has the form

$$A_0 + A_1 \cos \theta + A_2 \cos 2\theta + \cdots + A_n \cos n\theta + \cdots$$
$$+ B_1 \sin \theta + B_2 \sin 2\theta + \cdots + B_n \sin n\theta + \cdots,$$

where the A's and B's are constants. It is clear that on every circle where r is constant, the real part of (1) and the coefficient of i in (1) are trigonometric series in θ. The examination of the behavior of a power series on its circle of convergence leads to the subject of the convergence of trigonometric series.

45. Operations with infinite series. The value of an infinite series has been defined as the limit of the sequence of sums $s_1, s_2, \ldots, s_n, \ldots$ In computing with infinite series we must find how far such a limit of sums has properties possessed by finite sums. Can infinite series be added, term to term? Do the associative and commutative laws hold as for finite sums? How are we to multiply one series by another? Our answers to these questions for complex series are formally the same as for real series. Thus two convergent series can be added, term to term; the new series will have a value equal to the sum of the values of the two series whose terms were added. We can insert parentheses in a convergent series, and its value will not be altered. However, the series

$$(1-1)+(1-1)+ \cdots ,$$

whose value is zero, gives an example of a convergent series from which all the parentheses cannot be *removed* so as to leave a convergent series with the same value as the old; but if the series after removal of parentheses were convergent, then it would have the same value as the old.

As to changing the order of terms in a convergent series, this is evidently immaterial if the rearrangement involves only a finite number of terms, but if there is no limit to the number of terms interchanged, then, as with real series, the new series converges and has the same value as the old provided the original series was absolutely convergent. A convergent series which is not absolutely convergent can be rearranged so that the new series diverges, or so that it converges to a value whose real part is any number we please.

Proofs for the formulas for the product of two real

series apply with little change to the case where the complex series to be multiplied are absolutely convergent. To obtain mn terms of the product series we can multiply the sum of m terms of one series by the sum of n terms of the other. The infinite series composed of these product terms in some chosen order is itself absolutely convergent and can therefore be arranged in any order. In the case of two power series

$$f(z) = a_0 + a_1 z + a_2 z^2 + \cdots + a_n z^n + \cdots,$$
$$\phi(z) = b_0 + b_1 z + b_2 z^2 + \cdots + b_n z^n + \cdots,$$

it is natural to arrange the product series so that terms involving a common power of z are brought together. We thus have

$$f(z)\phi(z) = a_0 b_0 + (a_0 b_1 + a_1 b_0)z + \cdots$$
$$+ (a_0 b_n + a_1 b_{n-1} + \cdots + a_n b_0)z^n + \cdots.$$

If the series for $f(z)$ converges at every point within a circle about the origin of radius r_1, and that for $\phi(z)$ within a similar circle of radius r_2, the product series will converge and be equal to $f(z)\phi(z)$ within the smaller of these circles (and in some cases within a larger circle).

46. Series whose terms are continuous functions; uniform convergence. With series each of whose terms is a function, we next consider operations involving limits. If such a series is written

$$(2) \quad F(z) = f_0(z) + f_1(z) + f_2(z) + \cdots + f_n(z) + \cdots,$$

and the series is convergent for every point z of a region T throughout which each of the functions f is defined and is single-valued and continuous, a first question which arises is whether $F(z)$ must also be continuous throughout T. For each point z_0 of T we would then have

$$(3) \qquad \lim_{z=z_0} F(z) = F(z_0) .$$

Now $F(z)$ is the limit as n becomes infinite of $s_n(z)$, the sum of n terms of series (2). Hence (3) can be written

$$(4) \qquad \lim_{z=z_0} \left[\lim_{n=\infty} s_n(z) \right] = \lim_{n=\infty} s_n(z_0) = \lim_{n=\infty} \left[\lim_{z=z_0} s_n(z) \right] .$$

We have here a question regarding the interchange of order in an *iterated limit* for a function of two variables, n and z. That formula (4) does not always hold is shown by taking $z_0 = 0$ and

$$(5) \qquad s_n(z) = \frac{nx^2 - 1}{nx^2 + 1}$$

where x is the real part of z. This function $s_n(z)$ is a single-valued and continuous function of z. Its iterated limit, as n becomes infinite and then x approaches zero, has the value $+1$; the iterated limit in the other order is -1.

We now return to the examination of conditions under which (3) may be true, and we begin by re-writing (3) in the form

$$\lim_{z=z_0} |F(z) - F(z_0)| = 0 .$$

Since we have

$$F(z) - F(z_0) = [F(z) - s_n(z)] + [s_n(z) - s_n(z_0)] + [s_n(z_0) - F(z_0)] ,$$

it follows from a theorem of page 15 that

$$(6) \quad |F(z) - F(z_0)| \leqq |F(z) - s_n(z)| + |s_n(z) - s_n(z_0)|$$
$$+ |s_n(z_0) - F(z_0)| .$$

If the right side of (6) can be made less than any pre-assigned positive constant for all z sufficiently near z_0, then (3) will be true and $F(z)$ will be continuous at z_0.

Let us now see under what conditions we can make each of the three terms on the right of (6) arbitrarily small. Since, by hypothesis, the series (2) is convergent at z_0, it is clear that we have only to take n large in order to make $|s_n(z_0) - F(z_0)|$ as small as we please. Having taken some particular n that thus suits our purpose, we note that $s_n(z)$ is a finite sum of continuous functions, so that if z is only sufficiently near z_0 we can take $|s_n(z) - s_n(z_0)|$ as small as we please. It remains to consider the first term on the right side of (6). Since

$$| F(z) - s_n(z) | = | s_n(z) - F(z) |$$

we see that the value of the last term on the right side of (6) is that of the first when $z = z_0$. Hence, if for all points z of a region including z_0 and for each positive number ϵ there always exists an n which makes $|F(z) - s_n(z)|$ less than ϵ, *and if the same number n serves for every z in the region*, then we can make the right side of (6) less than the arbitrarily small number 3ϵ by choosing n so large that the first and last terms are each less than ϵ, and z so near z_0 that the middle term is also less than ϵ. When this condition is satisfied $F(z)$ is continuous at z_0.

Let us vary slightly the condition proposed above and require that for each positive constant ϵ a positive integer m exists, such that, no matter where z is in the region T, we will have $|F(z) - s_n(z)| < \epsilon$ for all $n > m$. The series (2) is then said to be *uniformly convergent* throughout T, and obviously the condition given in the preceding paragraph is satisfied if z_0 is within T. We conclude that *a series* (2) *whose terms are all continuous at each point of a region* T, *and which is uniformly convergent throughout that region, has for its sum a function continuous at each interior point of* T.

Note that uniform convergence throughout T demands more than convergence at each point of T. For the latter the inequality

$$| F(z) - s_n(z) | < \epsilon$$

is to hold for all n greater than some m, but m in general depends upon z as well as ϵ. For uniform convergence we require that there exist an m which does not depend on z, but on ϵ only; the same m can be used for all values of z in T. An example of a series which is convergent but not uniformly convergent is given by

$$s_1(z) + [s_2(z) - s_1(z)] + \cdots + [s_n(z) - s_{n-1}(z)] + \cdots,$$

where for each value of n the function $s_n(z)$ has the value given in formula (5). The sum of n terms of this series is $s_n(z)$ as there defined, and the sum of the series is $+1$ except for $x = 0$, when it is -1. The terms are continuous functions, and the series converges everywhere, but the sum is discontinuous at all points of the line $x = 0$; hence we conclude from the italicized theorem above that the series cannot be uniformly convergent throughout a region containing within it points of the line $x = 0$. It will be a useful exercise for the reader to verify directly that the inequalities defining uniform convergence cannot hold in this case.

Perhaps the simplest criterion for uniform convergence is the Weierstrass test, which states that a series (2) is uniformly convergent throughout a region T if there is a convergent series of positive constants,

$$M_0 + M_1 + M_2 + \cdots + M_n + \cdots ,$$

such that for each value of n we have

$$|f_n(z)| < M_n$$

throughout T. The proof is simple but we shall not stop to give it here. Let us note, however, the application of this test to the power series (1). If such a series converges absolutely for $z = Z$ (and we have seen that such a Z may be taken as any point within the circle of convergence), then Weierstrass' test applies to the region within the circle about the origin through Z, for we may take $|c_n| \, |Z|^n$ as M_n.

A power series is uniformly convergent within every circle about the origin that is within its circle of convergence.

It follows that a function represented by a power series must be continuous at every point within the circle of convergence. An important corollary is contained in the statement that two power series cannot converge and be equal for each member of an infinite sequence of values of z that has zero for its limit unless their corresponding coefficients are equal. For if

$$c_0 + c_1 z + c_2 z^2 + \cdots = b_0 + b_1 z + b_2 z^2 + \cdots ,$$

on such a sequence they are equal for $z = 0$, since both series represent functions continuous at the origin, and in consequence we have $c_0 = b_0$. Cancel these terms and divide the resulting equation by z. Then we have

$$c_1 + c_2 z + c_3 z^2 + \cdots = b_1 + b_2 z + b_3 z^2 + \cdots ,$$

a relation true for every point of the original sequence except, possibly, $z = 0$. These two series converge throughout the same regions as the original series, hence the argument of continuity at $z = 0$ applies again, and it follows that $c_1 = b_1$. Similarly we may proceed to show that each c is equal to the corresponding b.

47. Integration and differentiation of uniformly convergent series. Another important property of uniformly convergent series of continuous functions is that they can be integrated term by term. That is, if the series (2) has each term continuous in a region T throughout which the series converges uniformly, and if C is a curve all of whose points are interior to T, then

$$(7) \qquad \int_C F(z)dz = \int_C f_0(z)dz + \int_C f_1(z)dz + \int_C f_2(z)dz + \cdots \cdots .$$

This follows because, if S_n designates the sum of the first n terms on the right, we have

$$S_n = \int_C s_n(z)dz ,$$

so that

$$\int_C F(z)dz - S_n = \int_C F(z)dz - \int_C s_n(z)dz$$
$$= \int_C [F(z) - s_n(z)]dz .$$

If the series (2) is uniformly convergent, the absolute value of the last integrand can be made less than any positive constant ϵ, and in accordance with formula (3), page 89, the absolute value of the last integral will be less than ϵ multiplied by the length of C; that is, it is less than any preassigned positive constant if n is sufficiently large. Thus the value of the integrated series (7), which is the limit of S_n, is the integral of $F(z)$.

If each of the terms of series (2) is analytic throughout T, and C is a closed curve bounding a closed simply connected region all of whose points belong to T, then each term of (7) vanishes, by Cauchy's integral theorem, so that the integral of $F(z)$ must also vanish. If z is an interior point of T, it has a simply connected neighborhood wholly within T; the integral of $F(z)$ around every closed curve C within this region is then zero, and by Morera's theorem (p. 94) $F(z)$ is analytic throughout the simply connected neighborhood of z. Since z was any point within T it follows that *a series of functions each of which is analytic throughout T represents a function analytic throughout the interior of T provided the series is uniformly convergent throughout every region interior to T.*

We might expect that the derivative of $F(z)$ would be given by the formula

(8)　　　　$F'(z) = f_0'(z) + f_1'(z) + f_2'(z) + \cdots \cdots ,$

but we should pause to reflect that for many real convergent series (some of the more familiar Fourier's series are examples) the series of derivatives does not even converge. With analytic functions of a complex variable we may, however, express a derivative as an integral by formula (6) of page 99 for $n = 1$. To establish (8) for such series we substitute t for z in (2) and divide each term on both sides of the equation by $2\pi i(t-z)^2$. Integration of the resulting uniformly convergent series about a suitable curve C establishes formula (8). The reader will find it a useful exercise to write out a formal statement of this result.

A power series is a series of functions each of which is everywhere analytic, and the series converges uniformly throughout every circle within its circle of convergence, hence *a power series represents a function which is analytic throughout the interior of the circle of convergence of the series. A power series can be differentiated and integrated term by term; the resulting series will have the same circle of convergence as the original series and will be equal to the derivative and the integral, respectively, of the function represented by the original series.* In these respects then, a power series, which is the limit of a sequence of polynomials, has the properties of a polynomial.

As an application of some of these principles, let us solve by the method of power series the differential equation

$$\frac{dw}{dz} = w \ .$$

We have already obtained in Chapter IV a solution in the form $w = e^z$. If we assume that there is a solution represented by a power series

$$w = c_0 + c_1 z + c_2 z^2 + \ \cdots \ ,$$

convergent within the region T consisting of the interior of a circle about the origin, we have

$$\frac{dw}{dz} = c_1 + 2c_2 z + 3c_3 z^2 + \ \cdots \ ,$$

throughout T. These two series above are to be identical throughout T, hence their coefficients must be equal, and we have

$$c_1 = c_0 \ , \qquad 2c_2 = c_1 \ , \ \ldots \ , \ nc_n = c_{n-1} \ , \ \ldots \ ,$$

or

$$c_1 = c_0 \ , \qquad c_2 = \tfrac{1}{2} c_0 \ , \ \ldots \ , \ c_n = \frac{1}{n!} \, c_0 \ , \ \ldots \ ,$$

and with these values for the coefficients in the series for w we have

$$w = c_0 \left[1 + z + \frac{1}{2!}z^2 + \cdots + \frac{1}{n!}z^n + \cdots \right].$$

This last series converges everywhere, as the ratio test shows. So far we have shown that a power-series solution, *if one exists*, can have *only* the foregoing form, but we may now go back with the foregoing series, substitute it, and show that it actually satisfies the equation.

In the same way we can determine the coefficients of a power series which formally satisfies the more general linear differential equation

$$\frac{d^n w}{dz^n} + p_1(z)\frac{d^{n-1}w}{dz^{n-1}} + \cdots + p_n(z)w = 0$$

where $p_1(z)$, $p_2(z)$, $\ldots$, $p_n(z)$, are analytic throughout a circle T with center at the origin, but the power series so determined cannot be called a solution until its convergence has been investigated. It can be proved, however, that such a power series converges throughout T, and the validity of this method of solution is thus established.

48. Taylor's and Maclaurin's series. Near the close of Chapter VI we discussed Taylor's theorem with remainder, expressed by the formula

$$f(z) = f(a) + f'(a)(z-a) + \frac{f''(a)}{2!}(z-a)^2 + \cdots$$
$$+ \frac{f^{(n-1)}(a)}{(n-1)!}(z-a)^{n-1} + R_n,$$

and observed that when z is any point interior to a circle C about a such that C and the region within it are interior

to a region T throughout which $f(z)$ is analytic, then the
limit of R_n is zero as n becomes infinite. In other words,
we have

$$(9) \quad f(z)=f(a)+f'(a)(z-a)+\frac{f''(a)}{2!}(z-a)^2+\cdots$$
$$+\frac{f^{(n)}(a)}{n!}(z-a)^n+\cdots.$$

The infinite series on the right, called *Taylor's series*, converges and is equal to the function at every point within
the largest circle that can be drawn with a as center and
such that $f(z)$ is analytic throughout its interior, or at
every point of the plane if $f(z)$ is everywhere analytic. If
we take $a=0$, Taylor's series becomes *Maclaurin's series*.

We have, in Chapter IV, defined a number of functions
of z in such a way that the formulas for their successive
derivatives are those for the corresponding real functions.
This is true of e^z, sin z, cos z, $(1+z)^m$, log $(1+z)$. Thus
their Maclaurin's series can be written down by changing
x into z in the well-known series for the corresponding
functions of x; the results are

$$e^z=1+z+\frac{z^2}{2!}+\cdots+\frac{z^n}{n!}+\cdots,$$

$$\sin z=z-\frac{z^3}{3!}+\cdots+(-1)^{n-1}\frac{z^{2n-1}}{(2n-1)!}+\cdots,$$

$$\cos z=1-\frac{z^2}{2!}+\cdots+(-1)^n\frac{z^{2n}}{(2n)!}+\cdots,$$

$$(1+z)^m=1+mz+\frac{m(m-1)}{2!}z^2+\cdots$$
$$+\frac{m(m-1)\cdots(m-n+1)}{n!}z^n+\cdots,$$

$$\log(1+z)=z-\frac{z^2}{2}+\frac{z^3}{3}-\cdots+(-1)^{n-1}\frac{z^n}{n}+\cdots,$$

where $(1+z)^m$ is so defined as to have the value 1 when $z=0$, and log $(1+z)$ is the branch of the many-valued logarithmic function which vanishes for $z=0$. The first three series converge everywhere, the last two within the unit circle about the origin. At every point within the region of convergence each series is equal to the function indicated, so the same must be true of the series and functions when $z=x$ and x is on that part of the axis of reals that lies within the convergence region of the series in z.

The establishment of the validity of Taylor's series for real functions of x is often a matter of some difficulty; here we have a method that gives information in many cases. Given a real Taylor's series about $x=a$ corresponding to a real function $f(x)$, this method consists in substituting z for x. The corresponding z-series will converge within the largest circle about the real point a within which $f(z)$ is analytic. This circle cuts out on the x-axis the interval of convergence of the real series with which we started; within that interval $f(x)$ must be equal to the value of its Taylor's series. We thus may conclude at once that the binomial series for $(1+x)^m$ converges and has that function for its value at every point between $x=-1$ and $x=+1$. On the other hand, a Maclaurin's series for e^{-1/x^2} would be impossible since e^{-1/z^2} is not analytic at $z=0$. The remarks of the present paragraph are closely connected with the discussion on pages 3 and 104.

Let us return to the point that substitution of z for x in Taylor's series solves a problem of which we considered some cases in Chapter IV, that of defining an analytic function of z which reduces to a familiar real function of

x when z is replaced by the real variable x. If the real function $f(x)$ is representable by a real Taylor's series having an interval of convergence from $a-R$ to $a+R$, then by changing x into z we have a power series in $(z-a)$ converging throughout a circle about a of radius R and thus representing a function analytic within that circle and equal to $f(x)$ when $z=x$. *The function of z thus defined is the only one which is analytic throughout a circle about a and which coincides with $f(x)$ on an interval of the x-axis to which a is interior.* This follows from the observation that if there were two such functions they would be represented by Taylor's series whose values would coincide along the real interval just mentioned; hence by the argument of page 116–17 with $z-a$ substituted for z, their coefficients would coincide and the functions would be identical. Thus in Chapter IV, page 51, part (c) of our definition of e^z was superfluous. We need only have required that e^z be analytic throughout some region including a piece of the x-axis, and that it coincide along that real interval with e^x. If this interval included the origin we would obtain the series for e^z from that for e^x by substituting z for x, and this would be the only possible function satisfying the definition. Clearly we could have proceeded in the same way with $\sin z$ and $\cos z$, and with the branch of $\log z$ that is zero when $z=1$, in the latter case using Taylor's series with $a=1$.

It is frequently not necessary to compute the successive derivatives of a function to obtain its Taylor's series. If by any other means we obtain a power series in $(z-a)$ whose value at each point of some circle about a is $f(z)$, then this must be identical with the Taylor's series, coefficient for coefficient. This is shown by the argument of pp. 116–17 if we replace z by $z-a$. Thus, since power series are differentiable term by term, we could have obtained the series for cos z by differentiating that for sin z, and from term by term integration of the series

$$\frac{1}{1+z}=1-z+z^2- \cdot \cdot \cdot \cdot$$

we could write down the series for log $(1+z)$. Multiplication and division of series and substitution of one series in another also give short-cuts for obtaining Taylor's series.

If two functions single-valued and analytic throughout the region T interior to a circle whose center is a are

FIG. 20

equal to each other at a, and the same is true of their corresponding derivatives of all orders, then their Taylor's series about a are identical and the functions coincide throughout T. The functions would be identical even if T were not the region within a circle, provided only that a is interior to T. Briefly, the argument is this: The functions coincide within some circle about a. Suppose they were not equal at some point b within T. Connect a and b by a curve segment C interior to T. As we go from a to b along C we would first traverse a segment at all points of which the functions are equal; this would stop at some point c, beyond which every segment of C beginning at c would have points on it where the functions would be unequal. At c not only the functions but all their corresponding successive derivatives would be equal, since these derivatives may be computed by considering only values of z on C. Then the functions would be identical in some circle about c and hence they would be identical on a segment of C to which c is interior, contrary to our hypothesis regarding c. We conclude that there is no stopping point c and that the functions are equal all the way from a to b.

Similar remarks hold for two functions identical on a sequence of points whose limit is a. These results may be summarized in the statement: *A function single-valued and analytic throughout T is completely determined at every point of T when we either know its value and that of all its derivatives at an interior point or its values at the points of an infinite set having a limiting point within T*. This statement may be compared with the result obtained in Chapter VI, according to which an analytic function is completely determined within a closed curve by its values on that curve.

In older works one frequently comes across the phrase "the theory of functions according to Weierstrass." This refers to a method of developing the subject used by that author, though not originating with him, in which we start with power series as defining analytic functions and obtain their properties by means of operations with such series. In few recent texts is this method exclusively used.

49. Laurent's series. A first generalization of Taylor's series solves the problem of representing a function analytic everywhere outside a circle C by a series of positive or negative powers of $z-a$ convergent at every outside point. Some convention should be made here regarding the behavior of the function as z becomes infinite. The phraseology of Chapter V, page 68, is convenient. We shall call $f(z)$ analytic at the *ideal point $z = \infty$* if the transformation $w = 1/(z-a)$ carries $f(z)$ into a function $\phi(w)$ analytic throughout a neighborhood of $w=0$.

Thus if $f(z)$ is analytic everywhere outside a circle C about the point a, and is also analytic at $z = \infty$, and if $f(z) = \phi(w)$ when $w = 1/(z-a)$, then $\phi(w)$ will be analytic for all values of w interior to a certain circle about $w = 0$. Hence we shall have

$$\phi(w) = c_0 + c_1 w + c_2 w^2 + \cdots$$

throughout the interior of this circle. To return to the variable z, the function of $f(z)$ will be represented by the series

$$f(z) = c_0 + \frac{c_1}{z-a} + \frac{c_2}{(z-a)^2} + \cdots$$

for every z outside C including $z = \infty$, if we give $1/(z-a)$ the value 0 for $z = \infty$. This is often referred to as a *development about $z = \infty$*.

Without stopping to give explicit formulas for the coefficients in the foregoing series let us now pass to *Laurent's series*, which represents a function analytic in a ring bounded by two concentric circles whose center is at a point a. The inner circle may, in some cases, be allowed to shrink down to a; the outer may expand so as to include the entire plane.

Our starting-point is a corollary of Cauchy's integral formula sometimes called *Laurent's theorem*. If a region T throughout which $f(z)$ is analytic has a boundary C composed of two closed curves C_1 and C_2 that do not cut themselves or each other, and if $f(z)$ is continuous throughout the closed region consisting of T and its boundaries, then Cauchy's integral formula gives us for each z within T

$$f(z) = \frac{1}{2\pi i} \int_{C_1} \frac{f(t)}{t-z} dt + \frac{1}{2\pi i} \int_{C_2} \frac{f(t)}{t-z} dt ,$$

where the proper direction is to be taken along each curve. The first expression on the right is of the type discussed on page 89 and therefore represents a function $f_1(z)$ analytic throughout the region interior to C_1, the outer boundary of T, while the second expression represents a function $f_2(z)$ analytic throughout the region outside C_2, the inner boundary of T, and analytic also at $z = \infty$. The statement that $f(z)$ is the sum of two such functions, for all values of z within a ring bounded by two concentric circles with center at a, is Laurent's theorem, except that we need not suppose $f(z)$ continuous on the boundary circles, since any point within the ring T will lie in a ring T' interior to T. Thus $f_1(z)$ and $f_2(z)$ will have the desired properties with respect to every T' within T, and hence the theorem will be true for every interior point of T.

We have, throughout the region within the circle C_1,

$$f_1(z) = a_0 + a_1(z-a) + a_2(z-a)^2 + \cdots ,$$

and throughout the region exterior to C_2,

$$f_2(z) = b_0 + \frac{b_1}{z-a} + \frac{b_2}{(z-a)^2} + \cdots .$$

By adding, we obtain a representation for $f(z)$ convergent throughout the region common to the regions specified above, i.e., throughout the interior of the ring. This may be written, with a mere change of notation for the coefficients,

$$(10) \quad f(z) = \cdots + c_2(z-a)^{-2} + c_1(z-a)^{-1}$$
$$+ c_0 + c_1(z-a) + c_2(z-a)^2 + \cdots$$
$$= \sum_{n=-\infty}^{n=+\infty} c_n(z-a)^n .$$

The series in formula (10) is *Laurent's series*. As special cases it includes series in which there is a finite number only of terms involving negative powers of $z-a$ and others in which the number of terms involving positive powers is likewise limited.

Laurent's series converges uniformly throughout every region interior to its ring of convergence, hence it may be integrated term by term along a circle C' concentric with C_1 and C_2, and lying between them. This will also be true if function and series are divided by $(z-a)^{k+1}$ where k is a positive or negative integer or zero. As to the integrals of the terms of this multiplied series, the formula of page 91 applies, with a change of notation, and shows that the integral of each term vanishes except that of the term in $(z-a)^{-1}$. We thus have, for each value of k,

$$(11) \qquad \int_{C'} \frac{f(z)}{(z-a)^{k+1}} \, dz = \int_{C'} \frac{c_k}{z-a} \, dz = 2\pi i c_k \, .$$

This formula, for $k \geqq 0$, also holds for the coefficients of Taylor's series.

From formula (11) there can be obtained an inequality, which we will not write out here, corresponding to Cauchy's inequality for the coefficients of a Taylor's series.

Actually, the simpler Laurent's series are not usually obtained by using formula (11) for the coefficients. For example, to develop the function $(z-1)^{-1}(z-2)^{-1}$ in the circular ring about the origin whose inner boundary passes through $z=1$, and whose outer boundary passes through $z=2$, we may proceed as follows:

$$(z-1)^{-1}(z-2)^{-1} = \frac{1}{(z-1)(z-2)} = \frac{1}{z-2} - \frac{1}{z-1}$$

$$= -\frac{1}{2}\left(1-\frac{z}{2}\right)^{-1} - \frac{1}{z}\left(1-\frac{1}{z}\right)^{-1}$$

$$= -\frac{1}{2}\left[1+\frac{z}{2}+\frac{z^2}{4}+\frac{z^3}{8}+ \cdots \right]$$

$$-\frac{1}{z}\left[1+\frac{1}{z}+\frac{1}{z^2}+\frac{1}{z^3}+ \cdots \right],$$

so that the coefficients of the Laurent's series are given by the formulas

$$c_k = -1 , \qquad k < 0 ,$$

$$c_k = -\frac{1}{2^{k+1}} , \qquad k \geqq 0 .$$

For the ring bounded by the point $z=1$ and the circle of unit radius about this point, the foregoing function has the Laurent's development

$$(z-1)^{-1}(z-2)^{-1} = -\frac{1}{(z-1)} - 1 - (z-1) - (z-1)^2 - \cdots .$$

50. **References.** One of the best and fullest discussions of the topics of this chapter is given by *Pierpont*. Chapter II is devoted to series whose terms are real, and Chapter III to complex series, including power series. These chapters are, in the main, comparatively easy reading, and contain many illustrative examples. In pages 197–209 there is a discussion of functions defined by *steadily convergent* series, by which is meant series that satisfy the Weierstrass test. In pages 216–37, there is a treatment of term-by-term differentiation, and of Taylor's series and allied topics. Laurent's series are taken up in pages 234–37. The integration of linear differential equa-

tions by series is treated generally in pages 455–59, and is later applied to special equations.

Osgood does not go into elementary questions but devotes pages 81–107 to uniform convergence of real series. Pages 335–49 deal with power series and Taylor's and Laurent's series.

Goursat-Hedrick is brief on these points, since Volume I of the same work treats them for real series. Power series are taken up in pages 18–21, and in pages 78–88 there is a discussion of Taylor's and Laurent's series and other series of analytic functions. On page 39 there is an example expressing a series on its circle of convergence in terms of trigonometric series.

In pages 169–70 of *Burkhardt-Rasor* there is a brief summary on the convergence and divergence of complex series. Power series and Taylor's series occupy pages 199–215, and Laurent's series pages 247–54. The theorem that a uniformly convergent series of analytic functions represents an analytic function is proved in pages 260–62.

Townsend covers nearly all the topics here treated in his Chapter VI, leaving Laurent's series for pages 275–84.

Wilson devotes Chapter XVI to infinite series, those with real terms receiving most attention. Trigonometric series are discussed in pages 458–66. In pages 197–202 the integration of differential equations by series is considered.

CHAPTER VIII

SINGULARITIES OF SINGLE-VALUED ANALYTIC FUNCTIONS

51. Isolated singularities. A point at which a single-valued function has not a derivative, or in every neighborhood of which there are points at which the function has not a derivative, is called a *singular point* of the function. An especially interesting class of such points is composed of those possessing a neighborhood throughout which the function is analytic but which, of course, does not include the point itself. A point answering to this description is an *isolated singular point*.

It is useful here, for purposes of comparison, to consider the kinds of *isolated discontinuities* which single-valued real functions of a real variable x may possess. Such a function may, first of all, be not defined at a point $x = a$; or its value at $x = a$ may be given so that, although $f(x)$ has a finite limit A as x approaches a, we do not have $A = f(a)$. Thus if $f(x) = 0$ except at $x = 0$, then $f(x)$ will be discontinuous for $x = 0$ unless we add to our definition that $f(x) = 0$ at $x = 0$. If $f(x)$ has a finite limit A as x approaches a, a discontinuity due to no definition or an inappropriate definition of $f(a)$ is called a *removable* or *artificial* discontinuity. It remains to consider discontinuities due to the fact that $f(x)$ has no finite limit when x approaches a. A natural classification would distinguish between cases where, as x approaches a, first, $f(x)$ remains finite but does not have the same limit on all sequences of values of x whose limit is a; second, $f(x)$ becomes infinite on all sequences of values of x whose limit is a, but of which a is not a member; third, on some sequences of values of x whose limit is a the function $f(x)$ remains finite, while on others $f(x)$ becomes infinite. These three classes are illustrated, respectively, by the three functions

$$\sin \frac{1}{x}, \quad \frac{1}{x}, \quad \frac{1}{x} \sin \frac{1}{x},$$

defined as one pleases at $x = 0$.

When we consider a corresponding classification of isolated singular points of a single-valued analytic function $f(z)$, perhaps the most striking fact is that the analogy breaks down at one place; *a removable singular point, i.e., one at which there is a removable discontinuity, is the only sort of isolated singular point throughout whose neighborhood $f(z)$ remains finite.* This important result is sometimes styled *Riemann's theorem*. A brief proof depends on the properties of an auxiliary function $\phi(z)$ defined as follows:

$$\phi(z) = (z-a)^2 f(z), \quad z \neq a,$$
$$\phi(a) = 0.$$

We are assuming that $f(z)$ is finite throughout a neighborhood of a, an isolated singular point of $f(z)$. It follows that $\phi(z)$ is continuous at a. Further, the derivative $\phi'(z)$ exists at a and throughout a neighborhood of a; for

$$\phi'(z) = 2(z-a)f(z) + (z-a)^2 f'(z), \quad z \neq a,$$
$$\phi'(a) = \lim_{z=a} \frac{\phi(z) - \phi(a)}{z-a} = \lim_{z=a} (z-a)f(z) = 0.$$

Hence $\phi(z)$ is analytic and has a Taylor's development in a circle about $z=a$:

$$\phi(z)=\phi(a)+\phi'(a)(z-a)+\frac{\phi''(a)}{2!}(z-a)^2+\frac{\phi'''(a)}{3!}(z-a)^3+\ \cdots$$

$$=(z-a)^2\left[\frac{\phi''(a)}{2!}+\frac{\phi'''(a)}{3!}(z-a)+\ \cdots\right]$$

$$=(z-a)^2\psi(z)\ ,$$

where $\psi(z)$ is analytic throughout a neighborhood of a including a itself. If we now turn back to our definition of $\phi(z)$ it follows that $f(z)$ is identical with $\psi(z)$ throughout a neighborhood of a not including that point. If, then, $f(a)$ were *defined* as equal to $\psi(a)$, the singularity at a would be removed, and this characterizes it as a *removable singularity*.

One may wonder whence this difference of behavior between functions of a real and of a complex variable arises and why, for example, $\sin(1/x)$ has a finite discontinuity as a function of the real variable x while $\sin(1/z)$ as a function of the complex variable z has not a finite singularity at the origin. This last statement regarding $\sin(1/z)$ must, however, be true as a consequence of Riemann's theorem, since the singularity at $z=0$ is not removable. The answer is, of course, that while the function $\sin(1/z)$ remains finite as z approaches 0 on the real axis, there must be some other path of approach to the origin in the complex plane along which the function does not remain finite.

52. Poles. We next consider an isolated singular point a such that $f(z)$ becomes infinite on every sequence of points whose limit is a. The point a is then said to be a *pole* of $f(z)$. As a consequence of our definitions there must be a neighborhood T^* of a, not including a itself, throughout which $f(z)$ is analytic and at no point of which $f(z)$ vanishes. To deny the latter statement would be equivalent to stating that in every neighborhood of a not including that point there is at least one point at which $f(z)=0$ and hence that there are sequences of points approaching a on which $f(z)$ has the limit zero, contrary to our definition of a pole. The function $1/f(z)$ is also analytic throughout T^* and approaches the limit zero as z approaches a.

Let us now consider the function $F(z)$ defined as follows:

$$F(z) = \frac{1}{f(z)}, \qquad z \neq a,$$
$$F(a) = 0.$$

The function $F(z)$ remains finite as z approaches a, so that it can have at most a removable singularity at a. It is, in fact, analytic throughout a neighborhood of a that includes a, since it has been defined so as to be continuous at a. We may therefore represent $F(z)$ by a Taylor's series

$$F(z) = F(a) + F'(a)(z-a) + \cdots + \frac{F^{(n)}(a)}{n!}(z-a)^n + \cdots.$$

We know that $F(a)$ vanishes, but this will not be true of all the coefficients in the series, since $F(z) \not\equiv 0$. There will be a first coefficient not equal to zero, and we shall have

$$F(z) = (z-a)^m F_1(z), \qquad F_1(a) \neq 0, \qquad m > 0,$$

where $F_1(z)$ is analytic throughout a region including $z=a$. In fact, not only will $F_1(a)$ be different from 0, but there will be a neighborhood of $z=a$ throughout which

$F_1(z)$ does not vanish, since if it vanished in at least one point in *every* neighborhood of $z=a$, it would vanish at that point also, by continuity.

If we now return to $f(z)$, the foregoing relation becomes

$$(1) \qquad f(z) = \frac{1}{(z-a)^m F_1(z)} = \frac{\phi(z)}{(z-a)^m},$$

where $\phi(z)$ is analytic in a neighborhood of a which includes that point, and $\phi(a) \neq 0$. If we expand $\phi(z)$ in a Taylor's series about $z=a$, and divide each term by $(z-a)^m$, the result may be written

$$(2) \quad f(z) = \frac{c_{-m}}{(z-a)^m} + \frac{c_{-m+1}}{(z-a)^{m-1}} + \ldots + \frac{c_{-1}}{z-a} + c_0 + c_1(z-a)$$
$$+ c_2(z-a)^2 + \ldots,$$

where $c_{-m} \neq 0$.

Conversely, when formulas (1) and (2) hold, $f(z)$ has a pole at $z=a$, and this pole is said to be of order m. The expression

$$\frac{c_{-m}}{(z-a)^m} + \frac{c_{-m+1}}{(z-a)^{m-1}} + \ldots + \frac{c_{-1}}{z-a}$$

is the *principal part* of $f(z)$ for $z=a$.

Formula (2) is a special case of Laurent's series where the inner boundary of the ring of convergence shrinks down to $z=a$. If for such a region the Laurent's series about $z=a$ contains no terms involving negative powers of $z-a$, then $f(z)$ has at most a *removable singularity* at a; if it contains only a finite number of terms involving negative powers of $z-a$, then $f(z)$ has a *pole* at a: if it contains an infinite number of terms involving negative powers of $z-a$, the singularity must be *essential*, a term to be defined in the next section.

The phrase *pole of order m* may be compared with the term *zero, or root, of order m* which we apply to a point a when we have, throughout a neighborhood of a,

$$f(z) = (z-a)^m f_1(z) \qquad m > 0 ,$$

where $f_1(a) \neq 0$, and $f_1(z)$ is analytic throughout a neighborhood of a including that point. Under these circumstances the root a is isolated in the sense that a circle may be drawn about $z = a$ such that no other root of $f(z)$ lies within it, and the reciprocal of $f(z)$ will have a pole of order m in $z = a$.

53. Essential singular points. Under the term *essential singular point* we classify every isolated singularity of a single-valued analytic function that is not a removable singularity or a pole.

In order to see how a function may behave near an essential singularity, consider the function $e^{1/z}$, which has such a singularity at $z = 0$. We have

$$e^{\frac{1}{z}} = e^{\frac{1}{r}(\cos\theta - i\sin\theta)} = e^{\frac{1}{r}\cos\theta}\left[\cos\left(\frac{1}{r}\sin\theta\right) - i\sin\left(\frac{1}{r}\sin\theta\right)\right].$$

If z approaches the origin along any curve whose inclination to the x-axis at the origin is greater than $-\pi/2$ and less than $+\pi/2$, then $(\cos\theta)/r$ becomes positively infinite, and in consequence, the same is true of the absolute value of $e^{1/z}$, which is the factor before the brackets in the last expression for $e^{1/z}$. If, however, our path has an inclination greater than $\pi/2$ and less than $3\pi/2$, the limit of our function is zero, since this will be the limit of its absolute value. Finally, on a path with inclination $\pi/2$ at the origin we can take sequences of points having the origin as limit such that when any number $A \neq 0$ is arbitrarily chosen, there is a sequence on which $e^{1/z}$ has the limit A. Such a sequence is given by points whose polar co-ordinates (r_n, θ_n) satisfy the equations

$$\frac{1}{r_n}\cos \theta_n = \log |A|,$$

$$\frac{1}{r_n}\sin \theta_n = -\alpha_n, \qquad -\frac{\pi}{2} < \theta_n < \frac{\pi}{2},$$

where each α_n is one of the infinitely many determinations of the amplitude of A. *There are thus sequences of points having the origin as limit on which $e^{1/z}$ approaches any limit whatever.* We can say more than this. It will be noted that for each point (r_n, θ_n) indicated above the value of $e^{1/z}$ is actually A. *For each value of A except $A = 0$, the equation $e^{1/z} = A$ has an infinite number of solutions in every neighborhood of the origin.* But no value of z makes $e^{1/z}$ vanish.

The behavior of $e^{1/z}$ at the origin is typical of that of every single-valued function $f(z)$ in the neighborhood of an isolated singular point a which is essentially singular. For every complex number A there are sequences of points approaching $z = a$ on which the limit of $f(z)$ is A. The equation $f(z) = A$ has, one value of A at most being excepted, an infinite number of solutions in every neighborhood of A. This last proposition is a form of the famous *theorem of Picard* from which many consequences have been developed in recent mathematical literature. Its proof presents difficulties which place it beyond the scope of this monograph. The statement that there are sequences on which $f(z)$ has the limit A is more easily established. To deny this would imply that there is a neighborhood T^* of a not including a, and a positive real constant ϵ, such that throughout T^* $f(z)$ is analytic and

$$|f(z) - A| > \epsilon.$$

From this it follows that

$$\frac{1}{|f(z) - A|} < \frac{1}{\epsilon}.$$

The function

$$\phi(z) = \frac{1}{f(z) - A}$$

is analytic throughout T^* and remains finite according to the latter of the foregoing inequalities, hence it has at most a removable singularity at a. It therefore has a limit as z approaches a. If this limit were zero, the function $f(z) - A$ would have a pole at a, and the same would be true of $f(z)$, contrary to our hypothesis. If this limit were different from zero, $f(z)$ would remain finite in a neighborhood of a, and this is again contrary to our supposition that a is an essential singular point.

54. **Singularities at infinity.** The properties of $f(z)$ in a neighborhood of $z = \infty$ are, by definition, those of $f(1/w)$ in a neighborhood of $w = 0$, and this fact at once enables us to characterize isolated singularities at $z = \infty$. The transformation

$$w = \frac{1}{z}$$

makes the exterior of a circle about the origin in the z-plane correspond to the interior of a circle about the origin in the w-plane. We have already discussed on page

126 the development about $z = \infty$ of a function analytic at infinity; in our present notation this is of the form

$$f(z) = c_0 + \frac{c_1}{z} + \frac{c_2}{z^2} + \cdots + \frac{c_n}{z_n} + \cdots,$$

and is valid at every point exterior to some circle C whose center is at the origin. If the function has $z = \infty$ as an isolated singular point, then the region T outside a circle C, the point $z = \infty$ not included, corresponds to the region in the w-plane bounded by the origin and a circle C' about the origin. The Laurent's development of $f(1/w)$ in this latter region, when translated back into the z notation, gives us

$$(3) \quad f(z) = \cdots + c_{-n}z^n + \cdots + c_{-2}z^2 + c_{-1}z^2 + c_0$$
$$+ \frac{c_1}{z} + \frac{c_2}{z^2} + \cdots + \frac{c_n}{z^n} + \cdots,$$

and this series will represent $f(z)$ throughout T. If all the c's of negative subscript vanish, $f(z)$ has at most a removable singularity at $z = \infty$; if all but a finite number vanish, so that m is the highest positive power of z present, then there is a pole of order m at $z = \infty$; if an infinite number of c's of negative subscript do not vanish, then $f(z)$ has an essential singularity at $z = \infty$.

55. **Non-isolated singularities.** It is evident that we may have a great variety of non-isolated singular points. The definition of singular points at the beginning of this chapter is such that they may fill up curves or two-dimensional regions, or, when this is not the case, they may be limit points of infinite sets of singular points, isolated or not. Comparatively little research has been directed along these lines. We will here consider only two cases that are of some importance.

A function which has no singularities but poles throughout a neighborhood of the point $z = a$, this point not included, has a as a singular point if there are poles at points other than a in *every* neighborhood of a. The poles are then infinite in number and have a as a limit point. The function does not remain finite in a neighborhood of a, but this point is not a pole, since poles are isolated singularities. It is customary to extend the definition of the term *essential singular point* so as to include a point a of this kind which is not an isolated singular point. Sometimes, although this nomenclature is apt to result in ambiguities, such a point is called an *isolated essential singular point* because it is isolated from other essential singular points. An example of a function with this sort of singularity at the point $z = \infty$ is furnished by the function tan z, which has poles at the points where cos z vanishes, i.e., the points $z_n = n\pi/2$, where n is any odd integer. For an essential singular point of this sort, Picard's theorem must be modified so as to state that there are at most *two* exceptional numbers A for which the equation $f(z) = A$ fails to have a solution in every neighborhood of the point.

The other case to be mentioned concerns singular lines. With a little modification, Riemann's theorem on removable singular points may be extended so as to apply here. This gives a theorem which states that if $f(z)$ is continuous throughout a region T, and analytic throughout T except possibly for singular points which lie on a curve (of not too complicated a sort) then this exception is in fact *impossible* and $f(z)$ must be analytic throughout T.

56. Definitions of functions in terms of their singularities. It was part of Riemann's conception of a general theory of functions that both as a principle of classification and as a most suitable means of examining the properties of functions we should start from definitions setting forth a minimum number of essential characteristics. These definitions may involve functional or differential equations, but often they specify only the singular points of a function and the behavior of the function near such points.

As a first example, let us consider single-valued functions that are analytic at every point but one of the enlarged plane (for the meaning of this term see p. 68). This singular point, $z = a$, may be carried into the point $w = \infty$ by a transformation $w = 1/(z-a)$, hence we restrict our consideration to functions which are either constants or have but one singularity, and that in the point $z = \infty$. These are called *integral functions*. They are represented by ordinary power series convergent at every finite point; and conversely, such a series always represents an integral function.

If $z = \infty$ is a pole of order m for an integral function $f(z)$, the Maclaurin's series for $f(z)$ breaks off with the term in z^m according to our discussion of formula (3) on page 139, and $f(z)$ must be a polynomial of degree m. *A polynomial of degree $m > 0$ may be defined as an integral function with a pole of order m at $z = \infty$.* We define a polynomial completely, except for a constant factor, when we give its roots, with the order of each. By a well-known theorem of algebra, the sum of the orders of the roots is m, which is equal to the sum of the orders of the poles of the polynomial, since it has only the pole of order m at $z = \infty$.

Integral functions which are not polynomials have an essential singular point at $z = \infty$, and are called *integral transcendental functions* in contrast to the term *integral rational functions* often applied to polynomials. They have been extensively investigated, from many different points of view. The coefficients of their Taylor's series have been studied and properties of such functions have been given in terms of these coefficients. Another line of attack consists in a consideration of the behavior of the function in the neighborhood of $z = \infty$, and in particular the determination for a function $f_1(z)$, of *comparison functions $f_2(z)$* such that $|f_1(z)| < |f_2(z)|$ for all z sufficiently large. The generalization of the problem of expressing a polynomial in terms of its roots has formed the basis for a large amount of work on integral transcendental functions. When such functions have an infinite number of roots we are led to the expression of the function as an *infinite product*. To give but a single example, such a product for $\sin z$ is

$$\sin z = z\left(1 - \frac{z^2}{\pi^2}\right)\left(1 - \frac{z^2}{4\pi^2}\right)\left(1 - \frac{z^2}{9\pi^2}\right) \cdot \cdot \cdot \cdot .$$

The reader will find references to this subject at the end of the chapter.

Let us now turn to single-valued functions with perhaps more than one singular point, but whose only singularities in the *enlarged plane* are poles. For such a function these poles must be finite in number, otherwise they would have a limit point, finite or infinite, which would be an essential singular point. Rational functions

$$F(z) = \frac{f_m(z)}{f_n(z)},$$

where $f_m(z)$ and $f_n(z)$ are polynomials of degrees m and n, respectively, are functions of this kind. For let us suppose that $f_m(z)$ and $f_n(z)$ have no common factor which is not constant, and that $f_n(z)$ has the form

$$f_n(z) = a(z-r_1)^{n_1}(z-r_2)^{n_2} \cdots (z-r_k)^{n_k}, \qquad a \neq 0 .$$

The only singular points of $F(z)$ are $r_1, r_2, \ldots, r_k$, and possibly the point $z = \infty$. We may write

$$F(z) = \frac{\phi(z)}{(z-r_1)^{n_1}}$$

where $\phi(z)$ is analytic throughout a neighborhood of r_1 and $\phi(r_1) \neq 0$. Hence r_1 is a pole of order n_1, and similarly r_j is a pole of order n_j for each positive integer j up to k. The sum of the orders of these poles at finite points is n. The point $z = \infty$ is not a pole if $m \leq n$, for in this case $F(z)$ has a finite limit as z becomes infinite; in fact, if $m < n$ we say $F(z)$ has a root of order $n-m$ at $z = \infty$, since we can write

$$F(z) = \left(\frac{1}{z}\right)^{n-m} \Phi(z) ,$$

where $\Phi(z)$ is analytic at $z = \infty$ and does not vanish there. If, however, $m > n$, a similar argument shows that $F(z)$ has a pole of order $m-n$ at $z = \infty$. Thus the sum of the orders of the poles of $F(z)$ is $n + (m-n) = m$ if $m > n$, and is n if $m \leq n$. It is interesting to note that this is also precisely the sum of the orders of the roots of $F(z)$; for each root of $f_m(z)$ is a root of $F(z)$, and $z = \infty$ is not a root if $m > n$, so that the sum of the orders of the roots is m in this case, while if $m \leq n$ we must add to m the order $n-m$ of the root at $z = \infty$.

Are rational functions the only single-valued functions analytic except for poles throughout the enlarged plane? The answer to this question is affirmative, for suppose $F(z)$ has no singularities but poles and the finite poles (which must be finite in number) of $F(z)$ are r_1, r_2, ... , r_k, of orders n_1, n_2, ... , n_k, respectively. Form the product

(4) $f(z) = (z-r_1)^{n_1}(z-r_2)^{n_2} \ldots (z-r_k)^{n_k}F(z) = f_n(z)F(z)$,

the value of $f(z)$ at r_j being defined as the finite limit $f(z)$ approaches as z approaches r_j. Then $f(z)$ will be analytic at the points r_1, r_2, ... , r_k, as well as at every other finite point. At $z = \infty$ the polynomial $f_n(z)$ has a pole of order n, where

$$n = n_1 + n_2 + \ldots + n_k ,$$

and $F(z)$ by hypothesis is either analytic or has at most a pole there. Hence either $f(z)$ is analytic at $z = \infty$, in which case it is a constant by Liouville's theorem, or it has a pole at $z = \infty$. But a single-valued function whose only singularity is a pole at infinity must be a polynomial. Thus in all cases $f(z)$ is a polynomial, since even a constant is a polynomial of degree zero, and equation (4) allows us to express $F(z)$ as the quotient of two polynomials.

One of the earlier applications of the theory of analytic functions consisted in the investigation of periodic functions, i.e., functions which satisfy an identity

$$f(z + \omega_1) \equiv f(z) ,$$

where ω_1 is a constant, real or complex. We call ω_1 a *period*. Evidently any positive or negative integral multiple of ω_1 is also a period. If there is another period ω_2 such that for every pair of integers m_1, m_2, each of which may be positive, negative, or zero but both are not zero simultaneously, the expression $m_1\omega_1 + m_2\omega_2$ does not vanish, the function $f(z)$ is said to have two *independent* periods, and similarly for the case of three or more independent periods. A function with but one independent period is said to be *simply periodic*; for example, the function e^z is such a function with period $2\pi i$, while $\sin z$ and $\cos z$ have the period 2π.

The recognition by *Abel* of the fact that elliptic functions are *doubly periodic*, with at least one period that is not real, marked the beginning of a new era in analysis. Study of these functions has furnished some of the most important applications of the theory of functions. According to a theorem of *Jacobi*, there exists no *single-valued* periodic function (other than a constant) with more than two independent periods. A doubly periodic function not a constant, with independent periods ω_1, ω_2, must have one or more singular points within or on the boundary of a *parallelogram of periods* whose vertices are 0, ω_1, ω_2, $\omega_1 + \omega_2$, otherwise it would be analytic at every point of the finite plane and finite at $z = \infty$, hence a constant by Liouville's theorem (p. 99). An elliptic function is characterized by the statement that it is a *single-valued analytic doubly periodic function which has poles but no other singularities in a parallelogram of periods.* It will, of course, have poles in every parallelogram with which we can make a parallelogram of periods coincide by moving it so that its sides retain their lengths and directions, and it will have an essential singular point at $z = \infty$ which is a limit of poles. It can be shown, further, that a doubly periodic function cannot have a pole of the first order as its only singularity in a parallelogram of periods. The elliptic functions have at least two poles, or a pole of the second order, in such a region.

For examples of elliptic functions and proofs of the statements made above the reader should consult the references indicated in the next section.

57. References. Page references for the topics that have been treated more at length in this chapter are as follows: *Osgood*, pages 308–31; *Goursat-Hedrick*, pages 88–94, 109–11; *Burkhardt-Rasor*, pages 227–35, 254–56; *Pierpont*, pages 237–53; *Townsend*, pages 262–75, 290–95; *Wilson*, pages 479–84.

Picard's theorem regarding the values taken on by a function in the neighborhood of an isolated essential singular point is proved in *Osgood*, pages 703–10.

References on infinite products are: *Osgood*, pages 524–39; *Goursat-Hedrick*, Chapter III, Part I; *Pierpont*, Chapter VIII; *Townsend*, pages 308–17; *Wilson*, pages 453–56; *Burkhardt-Rasor*, pages 375–76.

Elliptic functions are treated in *Osgood*, pages 453–57, and parts of Chapters X and XI; *Goursat-Hedrick*, Chapter III, Part II; *Pierpont*, Chapters X, XI, XIII; *Townsend*, pages 317–26; *Wilson*, pages 467–75 and Chapter XIX.

CHAPTER IX

ANALYTIC CONTINUATION. MANY-VALUED ANALYTIC FUNCTIONS

58. **Questions regarding the identity of two analytic functions.** A function $f(z)$ is defined so as to be single-valued and analytic throughout a region T, and a function $\phi(z)$ is single-valued and analytic throughout a region T' that does not coincide completely with T. When shall we say that they represent the *same function* $F(z)$ over the two regions? As an example let $f(z)$ and $\phi(z)$ be defined by the following infinite series,

$$f(z) = 1 + z + z^2 + \cdots + z^n + \cdots,$$
$$\phi(z) = -1 + (z-2) - (z-2)^2 + \cdots$$
$$+ (-1)^{n+1}(z-2)^n + \cdots.$$

The first of these series converges throughout the interior of the unit circle about the origin, the second throughout the interior of a circle of unit radius whose center is at $z = 2$. These are geometric series; they are easily summed, and it turns out that each, in the region indicated, represents the function $1/(1-z)$. It is natural, then, to say that $f(z)$ and $\phi(z)$ represent the same function in the two regions; sometimes we say they are *elements* of the same function.

But let us be a little more critical about this idea. The mere fact that the same *mathematical expression* is equal to $f(z)$ in T, and $\phi(z)$ in T', is not enough. If $f(z)$ is analytic throughout the closed region T, and similarly for $\phi(z)$ in T', the boundaries being C and C', respectively, consider the expression

$$\frac{1}{2\pi i}\int_C \frac{f(t)}{t-z}dt + \frac{1}{2\pi i}\int_{C'} \frac{\phi(t)}{t-z}dt\ ,$$

and let us suppose that T and T' have no point in common. If z is within T, the first of these integrals is equal to $f(z)$ by Cauchy's integral formula. Since z is then exterior to T' the second integrand is an analytic function of t throughout the interior of T' and is continuous in closed T', hence the second integral is equal to zero by Cauchy's integral theorem. Thus the foregoing expression is equal to $f(z)$ for all z in T, and we similarly prove that it is equal to $\phi(z)$ for all z in T'. We are hardly ready to admit that two arbitrarily chosen analytic functions defined for different regions are to be regarded as the same function, even if a single expression gives their values in the respective regions.

Another example of this kind is furnished by the infinite series

$$S(z) = \frac{1}{1+z} + \left(\frac{1}{1+z^2} - \frac{1}{1+z}\right) + \left(\frac{1}{1+z^3} - \frac{1}{1+z^2}\right) + \cdots$$

which has $1/(1+z^n)$ as the sum of its first n terms. Since

$$\lim_{n=\infty} \frac{1}{1+z^n} = 1 \text{ for all points such that } |z| < 1\ ,$$
$$= 0 \text{ for all points such that } |z| > 1\ ,$$

the series has the value 1 at every point within the unit circle about the origin, and the value 0 at every outside point. Using any two functions $f(z)$, $\phi(z)$, we form the expression

$$\phi(z) + [f(z) - \phi(z)]S(z)\ ,$$

which may be written out as an infinite series. It has the value $f(z)$ within the unit circle, and the value $\phi(z)$ outside it. Thus there are expressions in the form of infinite series which represent in separate regions what we would prefer to call different functions.

A similar question arises when we consider many-valued functions. The equation $w^2 = z$ is said to define a *double-valued function* w of z. At every point except the origin w has two values, and in any simply connected region not including the origin the equation $w^2 = z$ has solution values for w which can be grouped so as to form two different single-valued analytic functions. The same statement is equally true of the equation $w^2 = z^2$. In this latter case the solution functions are z and $-z$, and we do not consider them as constituting one function. What distinguishes a double-valued function from two single-valued functions?

59. Analytic continuation. We shall find answers to these questions in the idea of *analytic continuation*. The foundation is contained in the theorem of page 125, an equivalent form of which states that if two functions are single-valued and analytic throughout a region T and are equal at every point of an infinite set with a limiting point within T, then they are identical throughout T. In particular, if they are identical throughout a subregion they are identical throughout T. We now consider two overlapping regions T' and T'', and we designate by T the region composed of all points that are either in T' or T'', or in both. Let $f(z)$ be single-valued and analytic in T', and $\phi(z)$ single-valued and analytic in T'', and let the values of $f(z)$ and $\phi(z)$ be identical at every point common to T' and T''. Then the function $F(z)$ defined as equal to $f(z)$ throughout T' and equal to $\phi(z)$ throughout T'' is single-valued and analytic in T. It follows from our fundamental theorem that $F(z)$, and therefore $\phi(z)$, is uniquely determined for a given $f(z)$. Under these circumstances we say that $f(z)$ has been analytically continued into T'' and $\phi(z)$ is its analytic continuation. This definition could have been so phrased that T' and T'' need not overlap, provided portions of their boundaries coincide.

The operation of analytic continuation may be kept up by the annexation of further regions. To guide our

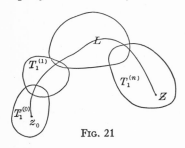

FIG. 21

notions, suppose two points, z_0 and Z, connected by a curve L, which may or may not cut itself. We cover L by a chain of regions $T_1^{(0)}$, $T_1^{(1)}$, $T_1^{(2)}$, ... , $T_1^{(n)}$, such as is shown in Figure 21. Each of these is simply connected, as is indicated by the subscript 1; each overlaps its successor; and the points of two successive regions form a simply connected region (but the points of three or more successive regions may constitute a region that is not simply connected). The curve L lies within the band thus formed; its initial point z_0 is in the first region $T_1^{(0)}$, its final point Z is in $T_1^{(n)}$, and successive partially overlapping portions of L lie in the successive regions. A function $f(z)$ is defined so as to be single-valued and analytic in $T_1^{(0)}$. Let $f_1(z)$ be its analytic continuation into $T_1^{(1)}$, let $f_2(z)$ be the analytic continuation of $f_1(z)$ into $T_1^{(2)}$, and so on until, if the process can be kept up, $f_n(z)$ is the final continuation into $T_1^{(n)}$. This process is called *analytic continuation along the curve L*. Each of the functions $f_k(z)$ is called an analytic continuation of $f(z)$, and each is an analytic continuation of every other.

The final function $f_n(z)$ obtained by the foregoing process is unique for a given L, but it is conceivable that by taking another path L' from z_0 to Z we should have obtained a different analytic continuation into a neighborhood of Z. For example, the equation $w^2 = z$ has a solution $f_1(z)$ which is equal to $+1$ at the point $z_0 = +1$, and is single-valued and analytic throughout a neighborhood of that point. There is another solution $f_2(z)$ which is equal to -1 at $z_0 = +1$. If

$$z = r[\cos \bar{\theta} + i \sin \bar{\theta}] , \qquad -\pi \leqq \bar{\theta} < \pi ,$$

we write

$$f_1(z) = r^{\frac{1}{2}} \left[\cos \frac{\bar{\theta}}{2} + i \sin \frac{\bar{\theta}}{2} \right] ,$$

$$f_2(z) = r^{\frac{1}{2}} \left[\cos \left(\frac{\bar{\theta}}{2} + \pi \right) + i \sin \left(\frac{\bar{\theta}}{2} + \pi \right) \right] = -f_1(z) .$$

For a path L such that $z_0 = +1$, $Z = +1$, and which has no point on the negative real axis (including the origin), each analytic continuation of $f_1(z)$ from z_0 around to $Z = z_0$ on such a curve is identical with $f_1(z)$ itself. But if we take instead the path L' consisting of a circle about the origin, as soon as we cross the negative axis of reals $f_1(z)$ becomes $f_2(z)$, or, more accurately, $f_2(z)$ is the analytic continuation of $f_1(z)$ across any portion of the negative real axis. As we complete the path L' back to z_0, our continuations now reproduce the function $f_2(z)$, so that on this path the final continuation to z_0 is $f_2(z)$, instead of $f_1(z)$ itself as on path L.

Let us note that neither of the two functions $f_1(z)$ and $f_2(z)$ in the foregoing example is analytic at the origin. In fact, their definition makes both discontinuous at each point of the negative axis of reals. It is true, however, that $f_1(z)$ can be continued analytically across any portion of the negative axis of reals not including the origin, the continuation being $f_2(z)$. But *there is no analytic continuation of $f_1(z)$ defined over the whole of a region to which the origin is interior*. In fact, a theorem which we give here without proof states that if $f(z)$ is any function single-valued and analytic in a neighborhood of $z = z_0$, and if there is a closed curve L beginning and ending at z_0 along which $f(z)$ can be continued analytically so that the initial and final values thus obtained for a neighborhood of z_0 are not identical, then there must be a point z' inside L and a path L' from z_0 to z' such that $f(z)$ cannot be continued analytically along L' from z_0 to z'. On the other hand, if $f(z)$ can be continued analytically along *every* path L interior to a simply connected region T_1, then the totality of the analytic continuations defines a function that is single-valued and analytic throughout T_1.

60. **The method of overlapping circles.** In order to continue a function single-valued and analytic in a simply connected region T_1, we must possess some means for finding another function single-valued and analytic throughout a suitable overlapping region T_1', and coinciding with the first throughout a common region. There are various methods, more or less general, for doing this, but perhaps one of the first to be thought of, and one which had much to do with shaping the notion of analytic continuation, was that connected with power series. Here a function $f_0(z)$ is given by a power series converging

in a circle with center at z_0, and we wish to continue analytically along a curve segment L which begins at z_0 and ends at Z. If the circle of convergence $T_1^{(0)}$ of the series for $f_0(z)$ does not include Z we take a point z_1 within $T_1^{(0)}$ on L between z_0 and Z and compute $f_0(z_1), f_0'(z_1), \ldots$, $f_0^{(n)}(z_1), \ldots$ We then use the Taylor's series for $f_0(z)$ about z_1 to define a continuation $f_1(z)$ into the circle of convergence $T_1^{(1)}$ of this new series. This process may be repeated for a chain of circles

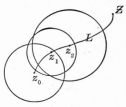

Fig. 22

$T_1^{(0)}, T_1^{(1)}, T_1^{(2)}, \ldots$, with centers $z_0, z_1, z_2, \ldots$, on L, each point z_i being inside $T_1^{(i-1)}$, and the last circle having Z as its center. If this method fails, $f_0(z)$ cannot be continued analytically along L from z_0 to Z.

61. **Monogenic analytic functions.** We are now in a position to consider the Weierstrass definition of a *monogenic analytic function* (the term *monogenic* has, unfortunately, also been used in another sense). Starting with a given *function-element* $f(z)$ defined so as to be single-valued and analytic throughout a neighborhood of a point z_0, we regard the totality of functional values defined by all possible analytic continuations of $f(z)$ as constituting the *monogenic analytic function* $F(z)$. Every function single-valued and analytic throughout a simply connected region and constituting an analytic continuation of $f(z)$ into that region is also an *element* of $F(z)$.

In the first example given in this chapter, $f(z)$ and $\phi(z)$ are both elements of a monogenic function which we readily identify by the expresson $1/(1-z)$. In the two following examples, $f(z)$ and $\phi(z)$ need not be analytic continuations of each other. As to the solutions of $w^2 = z$, these constitute a monogenic analytic function which is double-valued. In general, the functions defined by analytic continuation may be single-valued, finitely many-valued, or even infinitely many-valued, as is the case with log z.

A *branch* of a monogenic function for a region T (which need not be simply connected) is a function single-valued and analytic throughout T whose values throughout every simply connected subregion give elements of the function. In the case of the solution of $w^2 = z$, the functions $f_1(z)$ and $f_2(z)$ of page 151 are branches for the region consisting of the whole plane except the negative real axis.

Among the *singular points* of a monogenic function we might expect to class every point which is singular for a branch of the function. But let us recollect that in the case of the function defined by $w^2 = z$, the branch $f_1(z)$ is discontinuous at each point, other than the origin, of the negative real axis, although it can be continued analytically across this axis. Such discontinuities should not be regarded as singularities of the monogenic function, or even of the branch. Let us adopt a new definition as follows: *A point $z = a$ of the boundary of a region T for which a branch of a monogenic analytic function $f(z)$ is defined is a singular point of that branch provided an element of that branch does not admit analytic continuation to $z = a$ along a curve L all of whose points except $z = a$ are interior to T.* The point $z = a$ is also called a singular point of the monogenic function $f(z)$, but we should recognize the possibility that it may be singular for one branch and not for another. Under this definition are included all isolated singularities of single-valued functions except removable singularities, and there is also a new class of singular points, that of *branch-points* for many-valued functions. This term designates a point such that analytic continuation of some element on a closed curve about it yields an element having a common region of definition with the original element, but whose values in that region do not coincide with those of the original element, this being true no matter how closely the curve is shrunken to the point. For example, the point $z = 0$ is a branch-point for $w = \log z$ and for the solution of $w^2 = z$.

With this definition of a singular point it can be shown that the circle of convergence of a power series always has upon it at least one singular point of the function represented by the series. We shall not, however, give a proof here.

A *natural boundary* of a function is a curve every point of which is singular. It thus presents an obstacle to analytic continuation. Since a point may be singular for one branch of a function and not for another, it would perhaps be a better definition if we required all points of a natural boundary to be singular points of the same branch. An example of a single-valued function with a natural boundary is given by

$$F(z) = z^2 + z^4 + \cdots\cdots + z^{2^n} + \cdots\cdots .$$

This series converges for every point within the unit circle about the origin, but $F(z)$ evidently becomes infinite as z approaches 1 along the real axis. We have

$$F(z) = z^2 + z^4 + \cdots\cdots + z^{2^n} + F(z^{2^n}) .$$

If the roots of the equation $z^{2^n} = 1$ are denoted by $z_{n,k}$ ($k = 1, \cdots, 2^n$), then as z approaches $z_{n,k}$ along a radius of the unit circle $F(z^{2^n})$ becomes infinite, and hence $F(z)$ also becomes infinite. The points $z_{n,k}$, when n takes on the infinite sequence of values $1, 2, \ldots$, are present on every arc, no matter how small, of the unit circle, and they are singular points of $F(z)$. Thus every point of the circumference of the unit circle is a limit point of singular points and so is itself singular. This circumference is a natural boundary for $F(z)$.

62. **The permanence of functional equations.** An important application of these ideas is contained in what is sometimes called the *principle of the permanence of functional equations*. Suppose $f(z)$ and $\phi(z)$ are function-elements of the same function or of different functions, having a common region of definition T_1. Then if $F(z, w_1, w_2)$ is a polynomial in z, w_1, and w_2, the expression $F(z, f(z), \phi(z))$ will represent a function-element defined throughout T_1. If F is zero at every point of a line within T_1, it must be zero throughout T_1. For example, sin z and cos z are functions analytic in every T_1 and equal to the ordinary trigonometric functions sin x and cos x along the axis of reals. For real values of z, then, we have

$$\sin^2 z + \cos^2 z - 1 = 0 .$$

It follows that this equation holds at every point of the complex plane.

Let us now make the additional hypothesis that L is a curve with initial point z_0 in T_1, and that $f(z)$ and $\phi(z)$ can both be continued analytically along L into a neighborhood $T_1^{(n)}$ of its end-point, the resulting elements being $f_n(z)$ and $\phi_n(z)$, respectively. Then $F(z, f(z), \phi(z))$ is also continued along L, and its final corresponding element is $F(z, f_n(z), \phi_n(z))$. If F was identically zero throughout T_1, all of its analytic continuations will be zero, hence we shall have

$$F(z, f_n(z), \phi_n(z))=0$$

throughout $T_1^{(n)}$. To put this briefly, *if $w_1 = f(z)$, $w_2 = \phi(z)$ are solutions of the equation*

$$F(z, w_1, w_2)=0 ,$$

then all simultaneous analytic continuations of $f(z)$ and $\phi(z)$ are also solutions. This can obviously be put in a more general form where F is a polynomial in n variables.

A most interesting application is found in the theory of differential equations. If $w = f(z)$ is a solution in the form of a power series of a differential equation

$$F\left(z, w, \frac{dw}{dz}, \ldots\ldots, \frac{d^n w}{dz^n}\right)=0$$

where F is a polynomial in its $n+2$ arguments, then the successive derivatives of $f(z)$ have the same circle of convergence and admit simultaneous analytic continuation with $f(z)$, the continuations being the respective derivatives of the continuations of $f(z)$. Hence, in accordance with the principle stated in the preceding paragraph, every analytic continuation of a solution of the differential equation is also a solution.

63. **Branches and branch-points of many-valued analytic functions.** We have seen that monogenic analytic functions may be single-valued or many-valued. Their elements and branches are single-valued, and for many purposes we need study only the properties of such single-valued determinations, but other problems require wider

consideration. An especially interesting class of many-valued functions is that of *algebraic functions*, defined as the solutions for w of algebraic equations $F(w, z) = 0$, where F is a polynomial in w and z. If F is of degree n in w, to each z there correspond in general n values of w, and never more than n. Algebraic functions are finitely many-valued. The function

$$\log z = \int_1^z \frac{dz}{z}$$

is infinitely many-valued, and illustrates the fact that the integral of even a single-valued function may be many-valued. For a general study of functions defined by integrals a preliminary theory of many-valued functions is requisite.

We shall find it useful in considering the behavior of many-valued functions to include cases where $z = \infty$ is a branch-point or other singularity of a function $f(z)$. By definition, this means that the function $f(1/w)$ has the corresponding singularity at $w = 0$.

In order to simplify the present discussion, let us suppose that the monogenic analytic function $f(z)$ has only a finite number of singular points in the enlarged plane. Each of these will be either a pole or an essential singularity for one or more branches, or a branch-point. We now draw through all the singular points a continuous curve L which forms the boundary of a simply connected region T_1 consisting of all the points of the enlarged plane except the points of L. Figure 23 illustrates two ways of doing this for the case of three finite singular points at A_1, A_2, A_3. The branches, finite or infinite in number, of $f(z)$ for the region T_1 we designate by $f_1(z)$, $f_2(z)$, ...

Thus for the function w defined by $w^2 = z$, the points 0 and ∞ are branch-points, the curve L can be taken as the negative real axis, and the corresponding branches are those given on page 151. Similarly the solution of $w^n = z$ is an n-valued function for which n branches may be defined for the same region T_1 used for the solution of $w^2 = z$.

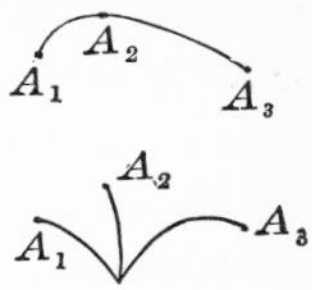

FIG. 23

64. **The monodromic group.** A question of primary importance is that of how branches continue into one another across segments of the *branch-cut L.* We can take account of this by means of what is called the *monodromic group.* This we now proceed to define. From a point z^0 not on L we draw *loops* $l_1, l_2, l_3, \ldots, l_n$, around the singular points $A_1, A_2, A_3, \ldots, A_n$, a loop being a closed curve which does not cut itself and such that no singular point lies on it and one singular point and only one lies within it. In the case of the point at infinity, the corresponding loop has the point ∞ as the only singular point *outside* it. The positive direction on a loop leaves to the left the region containing the corresponding singular point. In Figure 24, page 162, a system of such loops is shown for a function whose singularities are at the three points a, β, ∞.

If we go around a loop once in the positive direction, starting with a function-element $f_{k_i}(z)$ defined for a neighborhood of z_0, the result of analytic continuation may be an element of the same branch $f_{k_i}(z)$. This will surely be the case if the singular point for the loop is not a branch-point; and even in case the singular point *is* a branch-point, though there must be some branch for which continuation about the loop gives another branch, it may not be the branch we happen to have chosen as $f_{k_1}(z)$. If, however, a single positive circuit around the loop changes $f_{k_1}(z)$ into another branch $f_{k_2}(z)$, then continuation over the same path of $f_{k_2}(z)$ must change it into a branch different from $f_{k_1}(z)$; otherwise the continuation backward of $f_{k_2}(z)$ over the loop would yield $f_{k_2}(z)$ itself, and not $f_{k_1}(z)$ as it should do.

Thus we shall have a set of branches f_{k_1}, f_{k_2}, f_{k_3}, ... , such that continuation positively about a loop changes each into its successor. If this set has only a finite number of members, the last must continue into f_{k_1}, and we have a *cycle* of branches whose changes into one another correspond to the cyclic substitution whose symbol in the theory of groups is $(k_1\ k_2\ k_3\ .\ .\ .\ .\ k_n)$. If we start with another branch not in this cycle, we get another cycle, which will consist of only one member if the branch continues into itself. In the case of a finitely many-valued function we would then have all the branches classed into mutually exclusive cycles, with corresponding cyclic substitutions, for each loop.

A complete list of the substitutions for every loop would enable us to compute just what substitution of function-branches would be obtained by analytic continuation over any closed path starting and ending at z_0, and not passing through a singular point. In fact, continuation on such a path is always equivalent to a succession of backward or forward continuations along the loops l_1, l_2, l_3, ... , l_n. The totality of substitutions on the branches $f_1(z)$, $f_2(z)$, $f_3(z)$, ... , corresponding to all closed paths beginning and ending at z_0 and not passing through a singular point, constitutes the *mono-dromic group* for the function, or it may be better to say for the branches $f_1(z), f_2(z), f_3(z), \ldots$ The substitutions $s_1, s_2, s_3, \ldots, s_n$, corresponding to single positive circuits about $l_1, l_2, l_3, \ldots, l_n$, are the *generating substitutions* of the group. If the loops are taken in a suitable order, continuation about all of them in succession is equivalent to continuation on a circuit which divides the enlarged plane into two regions, one containing all the singular points, the other containing none. As the latter contains no branch-points, each function-branch continues into itself when we go around the boundary. The corresponding substitution is the *identical substitution*. Symbolically, we have

$$s_1 s_2 s_3 \ldots s_n = 1 .$$

To illustrate these ideas, consider the solution of the equation $w^2 = z$, which has branch-points at 0 and ∞. A loop l_1 about the origin will also serve as loop l_2 about ∞ if the positive direction for the latter is taken as opposite to that of l_1. For the generating substitutions we have

$$s_1 = s_2 = (1\ 2) .$$

The succession of substitutions s_1, s_2, changes f_1 into f_2, then f_2 into f_1, so that f_1 finally continues into f_1, and similarly for f_2, so that $s_1 s_2 = 1$. For the solution of $w^n = z$ we have

$$s_1 = (1\ 2\ \ldots\ n) ,$$
$$s_2 = (n\ (n-1)\ \ldots\ 1) ,$$
$$s_1 s_2 = 1 .$$

Another example is that of a six-valued function $f(z)$ whose branches are defined as follows for the region T_1

consisting of the enlarged plane with a branch-cut proceeding from $z = a$ to $z = \beta$ and thence to $z = \infty$ but not

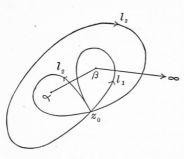

Fig. 24

passing through either
$a + 1$ or $\beta + 1$. We define
one branch of our func-
tion by the equation

$$f_1(z) = F_1(z) + \Phi_1(z)$$

where $F_1(z)$ and $\Phi_1(z)$ are
branches, for the region
T_1, of the functions defined respectively as so-
lutions of the equations

$$w^2 = z - a \, , \qquad w^3 = z - \beta \, ,$$

and are, to be specific, the branches of these functions
which verify the equations

$$F_1(a + 1) = \Phi_1(\beta + 1) = 1 \, .$$

The six branches of $f(z)$ may then be designated as follows
if ω is a complex cube root of 1:

$$
\begin{aligned}
f_1 &= F_1 + \Phi_1, & f_4 &= -F_1 + \Phi_1 \, , \\
f_2 &= F_1 + \omega\Phi_1 \, , & f_5 &= -F_1 + \omega\Phi_1 \, , \\
f_3 &= F_1 + \omega^2\Phi_1 \, , & f_6 &= -F_1 + \omega^2\Phi_1 \, .
\end{aligned}
$$

For the loops l_1, l_2, l_3, shown in Figure 24, we have

$$
\begin{aligned}
s_1 &= (1 \ 2 \ 3) \ (4 \ 5 \ 6) \, , \\
s_2 &= (1 \ 4) \ (2 \ 5) \ (3 \ 6) \, , \\
s_3 &= (1 \ 6 \ 2 \ 4 \ 3 \ 5) \, .
\end{aligned}
$$

The reader may verify that the succession of s_1, s_2, s_3,
corresponds to the identical substitution. For example,

s_1 changes f_1 into f_2, and this is changed by s_2 into f_5, which s_3 brings back to f_1.

65. **Monodromic groups of linear differential equations.** The idea of the monodromic group has been especially important in the theory of linear differential equations. For example, let us consider a homogeneous linear differential equation of the second order

$$(1) \qquad \frac{d^2w}{dz^2} + p(z)\frac{dw}{dz} + q(z)w = 0 ,$$

where $p(z)$ and $q(z)$ are single-valued and analytic with only a finite number of singular points in the enlarged plane. A fundamental theorem states that if (1) is satisfied by function-branches $w_1, w_2, w_3, \ldots$, which may be infinite in number and may belong to a finite or infinite number of monogenic analytic functions, these solutions can have no finite singular points other than those of $p(z)$ and $q(z)$. If two solution branches, w_1, w_2, are such that neither is a constant multiple of the other, then for each solution branch W there is a pair of constants, c_1, c_2, such that

$$W = c_1 w_1 + c_2 w_2 .$$

Now let us draw a branch-cut through the singular points of $p(z)$ and $q(z)$ and $z = \infty$, thus making explicit our definition of solution branches. When such a pair of branches (w_1, w_2) as considered above is continued about a closed path, it goes into a pair (W_1, W_2), which, according to the principle of the permanence of function equations, is also a solution pair. We must therefore have

$$W_1 = c_1 w_1 + c_2 w_2,$$
$$W_2 = d_1 w_1 + d_2 w_2 .$$

We are said to have performed a *linear substitution* on (w_1, w_2). If we consider the totality of the linear substitutions on this pair of branches which correspond to all possible paths of continuation, we obtain the *monodromic group* of the differential equation for this pair. It may contain an infinite number of different substitutions, but there is a finite number of *generating substitutions*, corresponding to the loops about the singular points. When we know the group for any pair, that for any other pair is readily obtained. In Riemann's celebrated paper on the hypergeometric function, the monodromic group for a certain class of equations (1) with three singular points was first investigated, and by the aid of this idea important results were obtained with such brevity and elegance that the whole theory of linear differential equations was thereafter placed on a new foundation.

66. **Riemann surfaces.** To the same mathematician we owe the geometrical representation of many-valued functions by means of *Riemann surfaces*. These have proved of especial value in the case of algebraic functions and their integrals. We may think of a Riemann surface for a function such as we have discussed in section 64 as generated by adding to the simply connected region in which an element is defined the successive regions in which its analytic continuations are defined. We thus may first fill out the region T_1, described in section 64, throughout which a branch is defined. Continuation across the segment A_1A_2 of the branch-cut may give an element belonging to a new branch; if so, the region we are thereby joining to T_1 is to be regarded as on another *sheet* over the z-plane, connected with the first sheet along segment A_1A_2. By further analytic continuation without

crossing the branch-cut we now fill out the region T_1 in this sheet and then cross the branch-cut segment A_1A_2 in the same direction as before. This either brings us into still another sheet or back into the first sheet. Note that we are allowing sheets to cross one another, but for a point moving on a given sheet in a given direction across A_1A_2 there are not two or more sheets into any one of which the point could go, but only one, which is determined when we know the one the point was on before it crossed A_1A_2. In that sense, all the sheets connected across A_1A_2 are not to be considered as having the same line A_1A_2 common. In this way we generate a set of sheets, each the *bearer* of a branch, each connected with its successor across A_1A_2. If there is a finite number of these sheets, the last is connected with the first across A_1A_2. If we proceed similarly, continuing every branch across each segment of the branch-cut, our continuation process either generates further sheets or it may connect sheets already obtained. The totality of sheets thus generated and thus connected forms the *Riemann surface* of the function. Each sheet is the bearer of a function-branch. If we know the generating substitution of the monodromic group we can tell how the sheets are to be connected.

For the solution of $w^2 = z$, with the negative real axis as branch-cut, there are two sheets, such that sheet 1 passes into sheet 2 and sheet 2 into sheet 1 along the branch-cut. For the more complicated function of page 162, for which a branch-cut and loops are given in Figure 24, the Riemann surface has six sheets, corresponding to the six function branches. From the fact that loop l_2 crosses the segment $\overline{\alpha\beta}$ but once we infer from the generating substitution s_2 that sheets 1 and 4 form a *cycle* at α:

that is, 1 winds into 4 and 4 into 1 as we go about a. Similarly 2 and 5 make a cycle here, and 3 and 6 form another. As to connections across the cut from β to ∞, we can figure them by considering either l_1 or l_3. For example, let us go backward around l_1. When we cross $\overline{a\beta}$ we replace f_1 by f_4, as we have already noted, but from s_1 we see that when we have come back to z_0 our final continuation is an element of f_3. Thus f_4 goes into f_3 across $\overline{\beta\infty}$ if we go around l_1 backward, or f_3 goes into f_4 when we go forward. In a similar way we obtain the other connections and find that in what we have called the forward direction across $\overline{\beta\infty}$, the sheets go into one another in the order 1, 5, 3, 4, 2, 6, 1, as might have been inferred from s_3. The surface has two triple windings, also called cycles, about β, and a cycle of six windings about ∞.

To locate a point on a Riemann surface we must not only give its co-ordinates but specify which sheet it is on, thereby indicating the corresponding branch. Thus a many-valued function $f(z)$ has but one value at every non-singular point on its Riemann surface. We are in this way enabled to discuss the conformal representation where w is a many-valued function of z. If z is a single-valued function of w, we map on the flat w-plane regions on the Riemann surface for $f(z)$. If z is a many-valued function of w, we have a corresponding Riemann surface over the w-plane and the relation is one to one between the two surfaces with the exception of singular points, so that we can discuss conformal mapping of parts of one surface upon the other.

Many of the theorems for single-valued functions can now be carried over to many-valued functions and be expressed in terms of the Riemann surface. In particular there are analogues for Cauchy's theorems on integrals when we take closed paths on a Riemann surface. Into all this we cannot go farther here, but the following remark will indicate an application of this theory. The elliptic integrals have, since the end of the eighteenth century, received much attention from mathematicians. With the rise of the theory of functions they were studied for complex values of the variables. Their integrands are, however, multiple-valued functions. Thus for the integral

$$w = \int_0^z \frac{dz}{\sqrt{(1-z^2)(1-k^2z^2)}},$$

the integrand is a double-valued function with four branch-points. If the path of integration goes about a branch-point, one branch of the integrand passes over into another. The Riemann surface puts all of this concretely before us, and by specifying integration as along a path on this surface we obtain a clearer view of the whole problem.

67. **A theorem regarding algebraic functions.** The Riemannian program for the study of functions, proceeding from a minimum of functional definitions, has been followed with much success for many-valued functions. We have seen in a preceding section that a single-valued function of z which has no singularities in the enlarged z-plane except poles is necessarily rational in z. This theorem has a generalization for many-valued functions which is a striking example of what may be accomplished by Riemannian methods. For a many-valued function the many-sheeted Riemann surface of the function takes the place of the single-sheeted z-plane for

a single-valued function.   In conclusion we quote without proof this generalized theorem:

An n-valued function $w = f(z)$ which has no singularities on its Riemann surface except poles is an algebraic function; that is, there is an equation

$$F(w\,,\,z) = 0\,,$$

where F is a polynomial of degree n in w and also a polynomial in z, such that whenever we substitute an element of $f(z)$ for w the equation is identically satisfied.

68. **References.** *Osgood, Goursat-Hedrick,* and *Burkhardt-Rasor* each devote a chapter to analytic continuation; these are Chapters IX, IV, and VI, respectively. *Goursat-Hedrick* is especially full on the subject of natural boundaries. *Burkhardt-Rasor* devotes several pages to the method of continuation called *reflection* on a line or curve. The same subject forms part of *Townsend's* pages 245–62 on analytic continuation, and occupies *Wilson's* pages 543–45. Otherwise *Wilson* has but a few words, on page 444, regarding analytic continuation. *Pierpont* (pp. 224–28) is only a little less brief.

Osgood's Chapter VIII presents an extended and characteristically critical and accurate treatment of Riemann surfaces, with examples illustrating methods for construction and conformal mapping problems, especially for algebraic functions and their integrals. A few pages are devoted to the monodromic group. *Burkhardt-Rasor's* Chapter V uses Riemann surfaces almost exclusively, with a number of examples. *Townsend* proceeds similarly in Chapter VIII. On the other hand, *Goursat-Hedrick* and *Pierpont* make no use of Riemann surfaces. The former gives examples of many-valued functions in pages 13–18 and 28–32, and in pages 114–22 studies integrals of many-valued functions by the loop method. Examples are also given in *Pierpont*, pages 89–102 and 122–28. Much of the latter part of this book is concerned with integrals of many-valued functions, and with many-valued functions which are defined as solutions of linear differential equations of the second order. *Wilson* illustrates Riemann surfaces in pages 491–96, and gives examples of integration on such surfaces in pages 498–502. The parts of Chapter XIX on elliptic integrals contain further applications of this method.

INDEX

(The numbers refer to pages)

PRINTED IN THE U.S.A.